This book is to be returned on or before
the last date stamped below

100% recycled paper

The Big Book of Movie Music

Order No. HLE90000165
ISBN 0-7119-6418-1

Exclusive Distributors:
Music Sales Limited
8/9 Frith Street, London W1V 5TZ, England.
Music Sales Pty Limited
120 Rothschild Avenue, Rosebery, NSW 2018, Australia.

Cover design by Pearce Marchbank, Studio Twenty, London
Computer layout by Ben May
Printed in the USA

Your Guarantee of Quality
As publishers, we strive to produce every book to the
highest commercial standards.
This book has been carefully designed to minimise awkward
page turns and to make playing from it a real pleasure.
Throughout, the printing and binding have been planned to
ensure a sturdy, attractive publication which should give
years of enjoyment.
If your copy fails to meet our high standards,
please inform us and we will gladly replace it.

Music Sales' complete catalogue describes thousands of titles
and is available in full colour sections by subject, direct from
Music Sales Limited. Please state your areas of interest and
send a cheque/postal order for £1.50 for postage to:
Music Sales Limited, Newmarket Road,
Bury St. Edmunds, Suffolk IP33 3YB, England.

Visit the Internet Music Shop at
http://www.musicsales.co.uk

Hal Leonard Europe
Distributed by Music Sales

784.89

AIRPORT LOVE THEME
(Winds Of Chance)
from AIRPORT

Words by PAUL FRANCIS WEBSTER
Music by ALFRED NEWMAN

MCA music publishing

BEAUTY AND THE BEAST
from Walt Disney's BEAUTY AND THE BEAST

Lyrics by HOWARD ASHMAN
Music by ALAN MENKEN

Bb7sus   Eb(add9)   Eb   Bb7sus   Bb7

ly.

Just a lit - tle change.

Eb(add9)   Eb   Bbm7   Eb7

Small, to say the least.   Both a lit - tle

Abmaj7   Gm7   Fm7   Bb7sus   Bb7

scared,   nei - ther one pre - pared.   Beau - ty and the

poco rit.

Eb(add9)   Bb7sus   Gm

Beast.   Ev - er just the same.

a tempo   *mf*

BABY ELEPHANT WALK
from the Paramount Picture HATARI!

By HENRY MANCINI

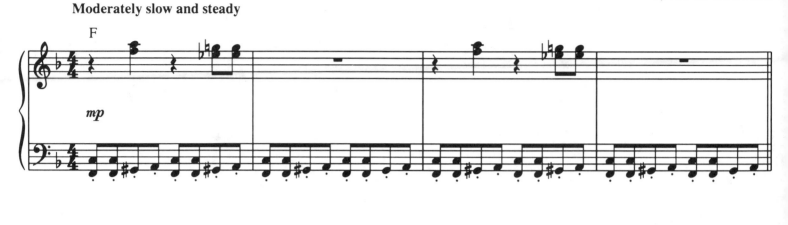

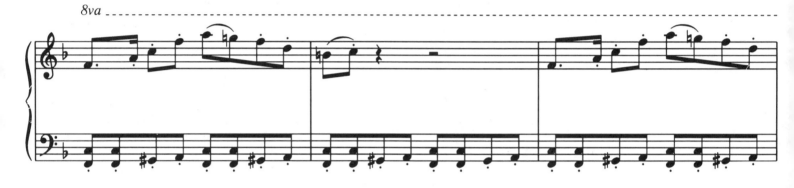

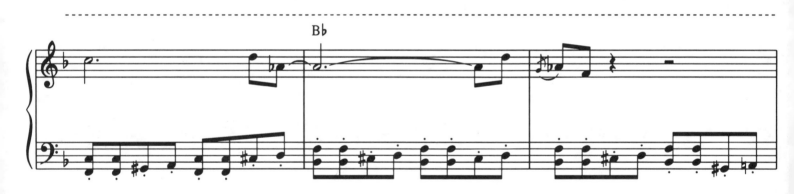

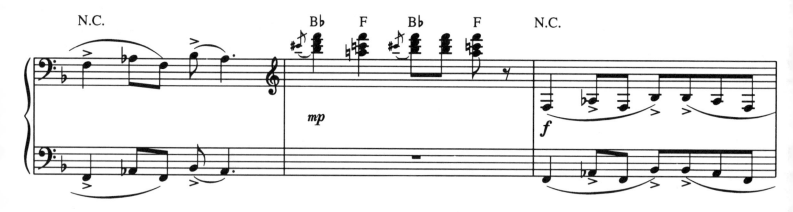

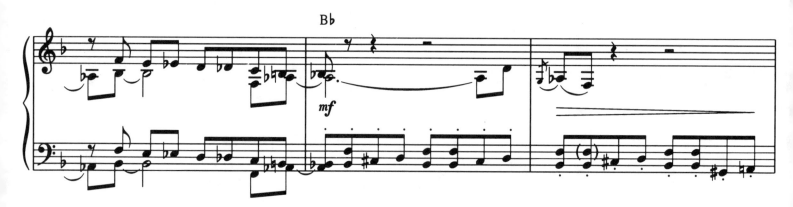

BEYOND THE BLUE HORIZON
from the Paramount Picture MONTE CARLO

Words by LEO ROBIN
Music by RICHARD A. WHITING
and W. FRANKE HARLING

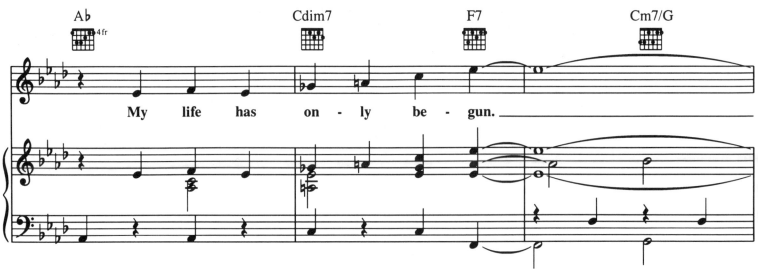

My life has on - ly be - gun. _____

Be - yond the blue ho -

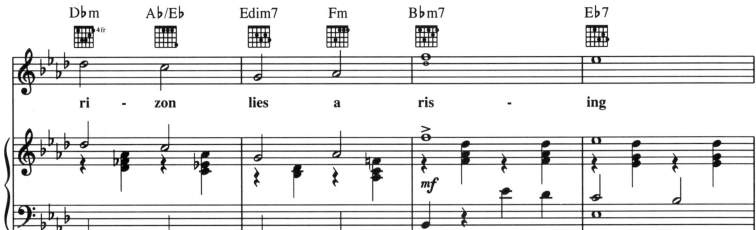

ri - zon lies a ris - ing

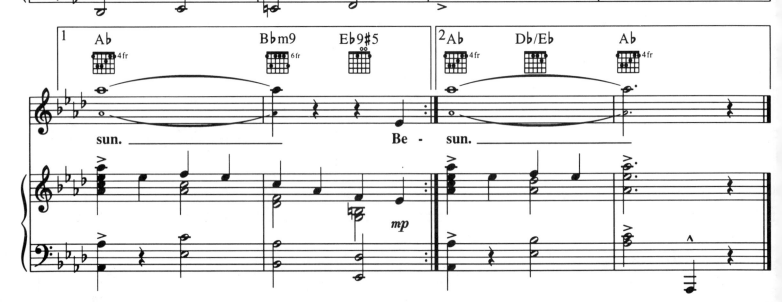

sun. _____ Be - sun.

BUTTONS AND BOWS

from the Paramount Picture PALEFACE

Words and Music by JAY LIVINGSTON
and RAY EVANS

Medium bounce

A west-ern ranch is just a branch of no-where junc-tion to

me. Gim-me the cit-y where liv-in's pret-ty and the

gals wear fin-er-y. _____ East is east and

BLUE VELVET
featured in the Motion Picture BLUE VELVET

Words and Music by
BERNIE WAYNE and LEE MORRIS

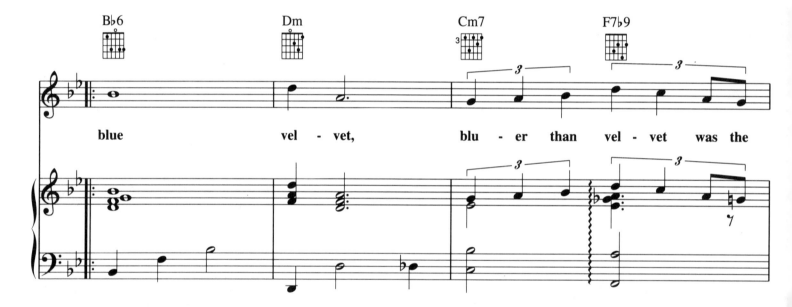

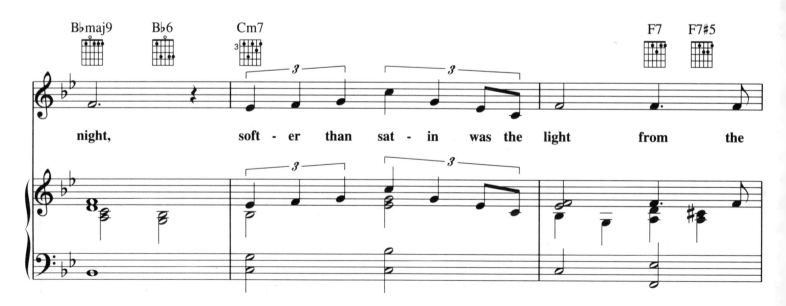

CALL ME IRRESPONSIBLE
from the Paramount Picture PAPA'S DELICATE CONDITION

Words by SAMMY CAHN
Music by JAMES VAN HEUSEN

CAN YOU FEEL THE LOVE TONIGHT

from Walt Disney Pictures' THE LION KING

Music by ELTON JOHN
Lyrics by TIM RICE

CHIM CHIM CHER-EE
from Walt Disney's MARY POPPINS

Words and Music by RICHARD M. SHERMAN
and ROBERT B. SHERMAN

CANDLE ON THE WATER
from Walt Disney's PETE'S DRAGON

Words and Music by AL KASHA
and JOEL HIRSCHHORN

DEARLY BELOVED
from YOU WERE NEVER LOVELIER

Words by JOHNNY MERCER
Music by JEROME KERN

Tell me that it's true, _____ Tell me you a - gree, _____ I was meant for

you, _____ You were meant for me. _____

Refrain-Andante cantabile, ma ben ritmato

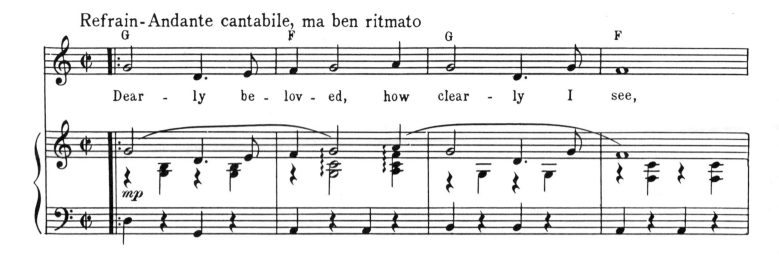

Dear - ly be - lov - ed, how clear - ly I see,

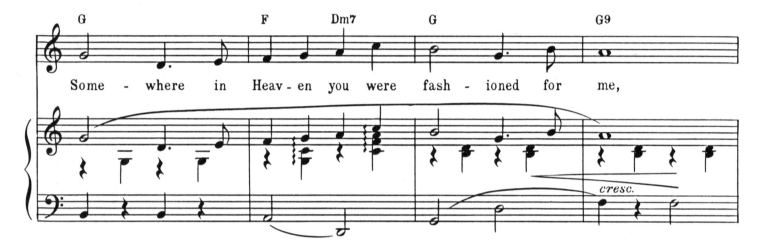

Some - where in Heav - en you were fash - ioned for me,

An - gel eyes _____ knew you, _____

An - gel voi - ces led me to you; _____

Nothing could save me, Fate gave me a sign;

I know that I'll be yours come show-er or shine;

So I say _____ mere - ly, _____ Dear - ly be -

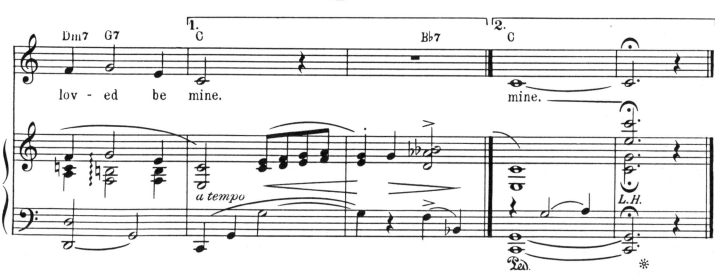

lov - ed be mine.　　　　　mine.

DOLORES
from the Paramount Picture LAS VEGAS NIGHTS

Words by FRANK LOESSER
Music by LOUIS ALTER

D

C

G

up and down ___ be - fore a cer - tain girl's a - bode.

Cm

Gm

And from a hun - dred lips the mel - o - dy came ___

Am7♭5   **D7**   **D7♭9**   **Gm**

croon - ing her name.

Refrain, Molto Moderato *(lightly)*

G

How I love the kiss - es of Do - lo - res;

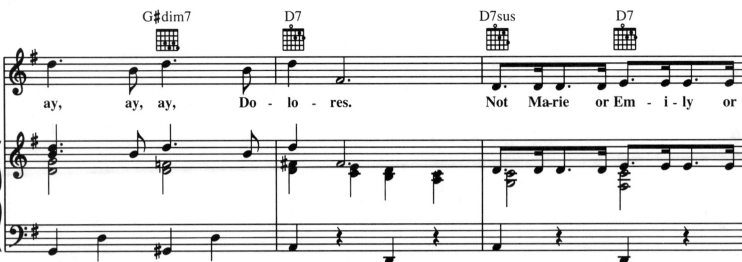

ay, ay, ay, Do - lo - res. Not Ma-rie or Em - i - ly or

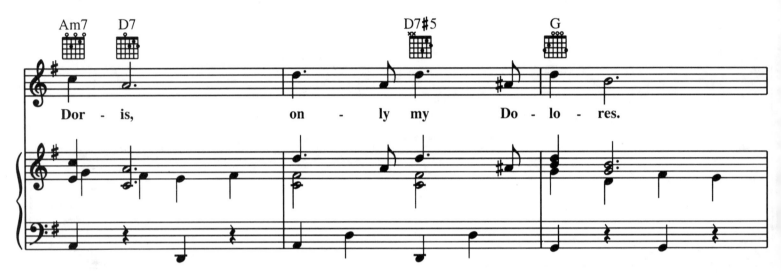

Dor - is, on - ly my Do - lo - res.

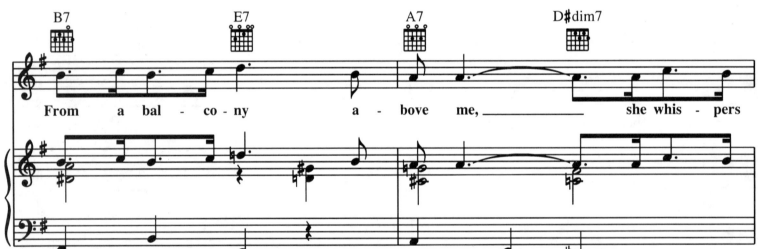

From a bal - co - ny a - bove me, _____ she whis - pers

"Love me," _____ and throws a rose. Ah, but she is twice as

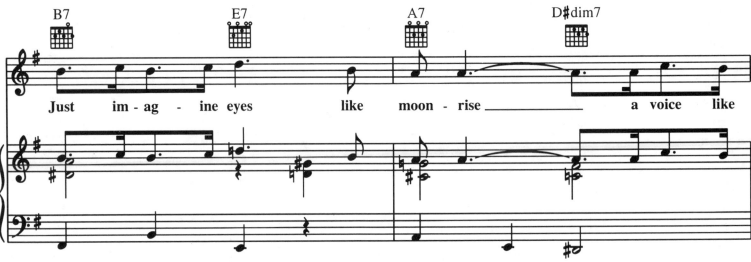

Just im-ag-ine eyes like moon-rise _____ a voice like

mu - sic, _____ and lips like wine!

What a break if I could make Do - lo - res

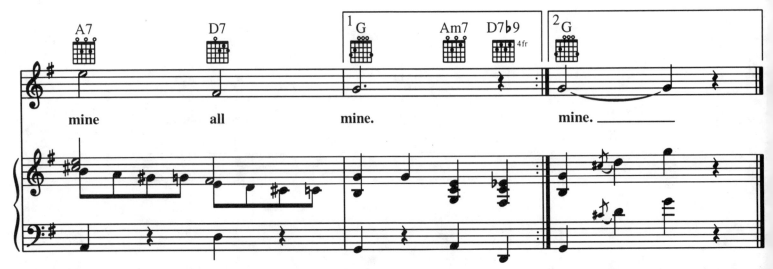

mine all mine. mine. _____

EYE OF THE TIGER
Theme from ROCKY III

Words and Music by FRANK SULLIVAN
and JIM PETERIK

Ris - in' up,___

back on the street,___ did my time,___ took my chanc - es.

54

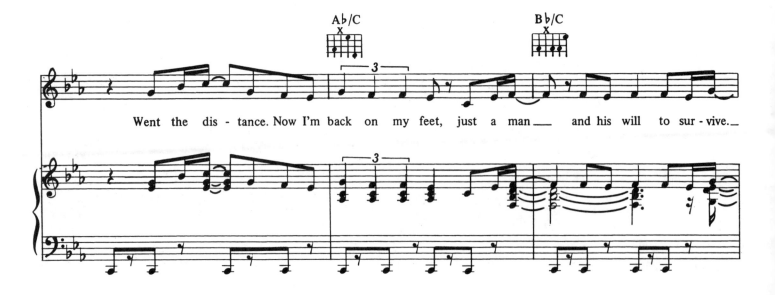

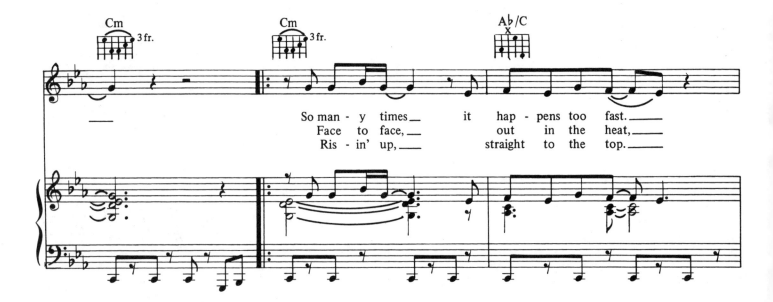

Don't lose your grip__ on the dreams of the past. You must
They stack the odds,__ still we take to the street for the
Went the dis - tance. Now I'm not gon - na stop, just a

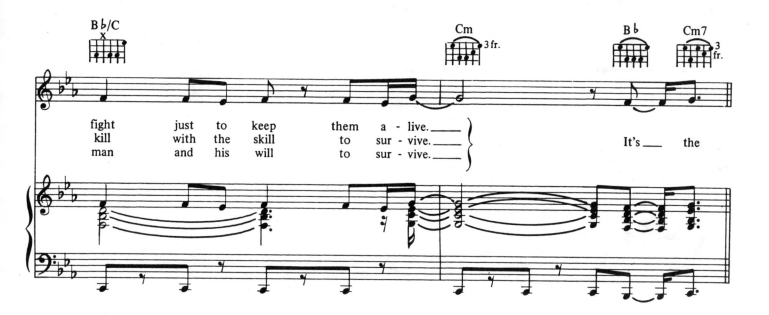

fight just to keep them a - live.____
kill with the skill to sur - vive.____
man and his will to sur - vive.____

It's __ the

eye of the ti - ger. It's the thrill of the fight, ris - in'

Repeat and fade

The eye of the ti - ger.

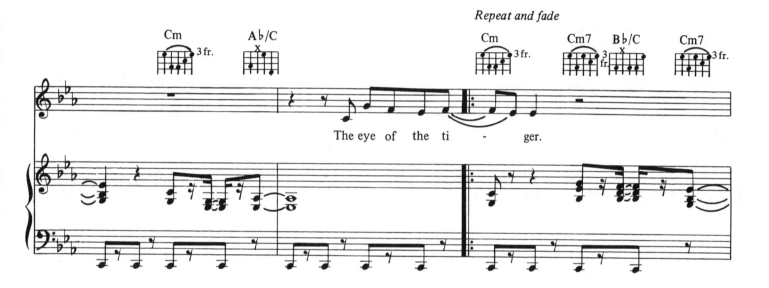

The eye of the ti -

FAR AND AWAY
(Main Theme)
from the Universal Motion Picture FAR AND AWAY

Written by
JOHN WILLIAMS

Moderately

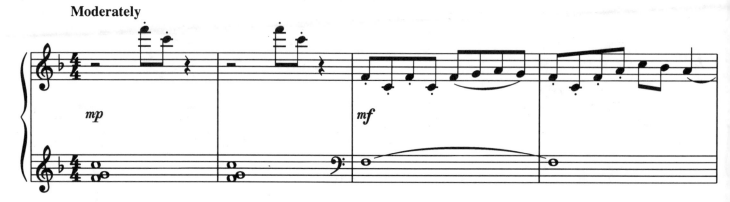

Sweetly, slightly slower

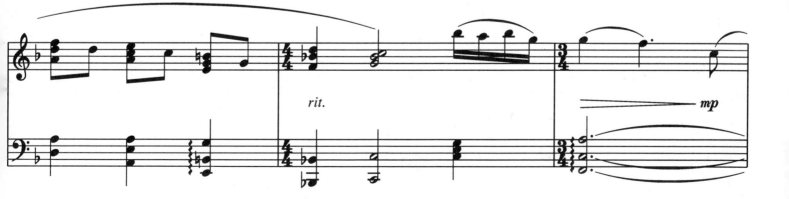

Piu mosso

Maestoso

Piu mosso

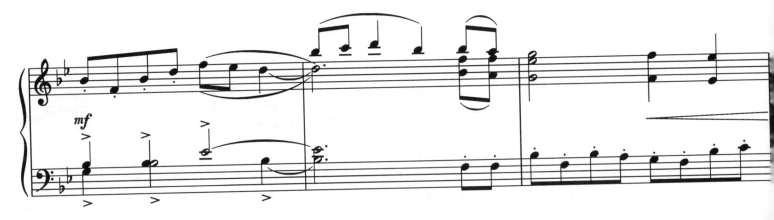

THE FOLKS WHO LIVE ON THE HILL

from HIGH, WIDE AND HANDSOME

Lyrics by OSCAR HAMMERSTEIN II
Music by JEROME KERN

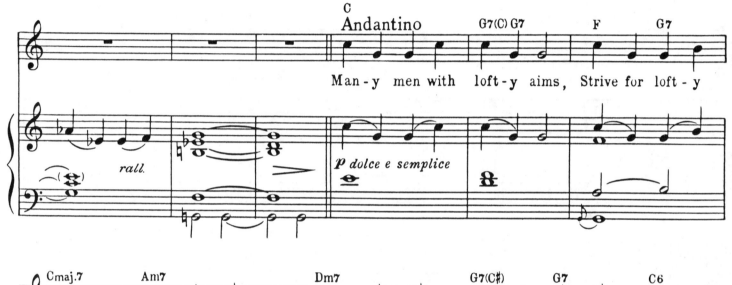

Molto sostenuto

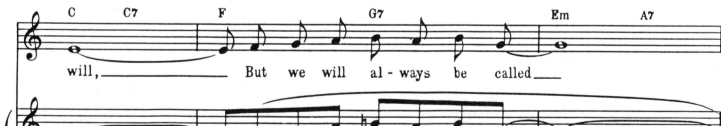

A FINE ROMANCE

from SWING TIME

Words by DOROTHY FIELDS
Music by JEROME KERN

C/E
E♭dim
Dm7
G7
Dm7
G7
clams in a dish of chow - der. But
thrills that a health - y crime has! We
C
E7
we just "fizz" like parts of a Seid - litz pow - der.
don't have half the thrills that the "March of Time" has!
Dm7
G7
C
C♯dim7
G7
A fine ro - mance with no
A fine ro - mance, my good
G7♯5
C
G7
clinch - es. A fine ro - mance with no
wom - an! My strong "Aged in the wood"

FOR ALL WE KNOW
from the Motion Picture LOVERS AND OTHER STRANGERS

Words by ROBB WILSON and JAMES GRIFFIN
Music by FRED KARLIN

Moderato, with a light beat

Love, _____ look at the two of us, _____ Stran-

gers _____ in man-y ways. _____

FORREST GUMP SUITE
from the Paramount Motion Picture FORREST GUMP

Music by ALAN SILVESTRI

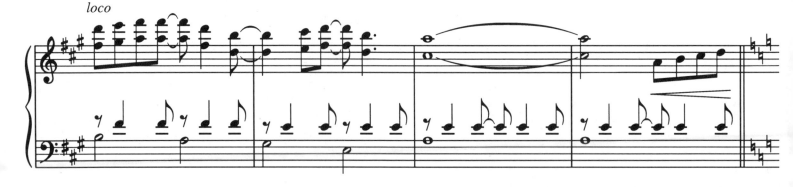

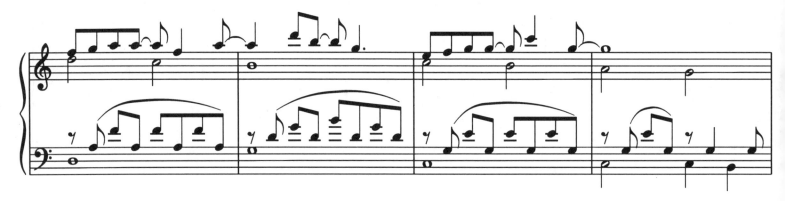

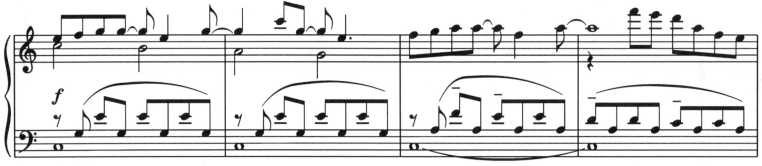

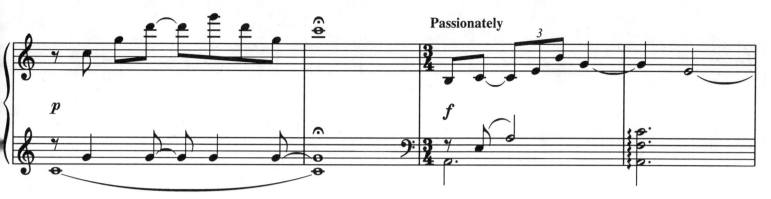

Passionately

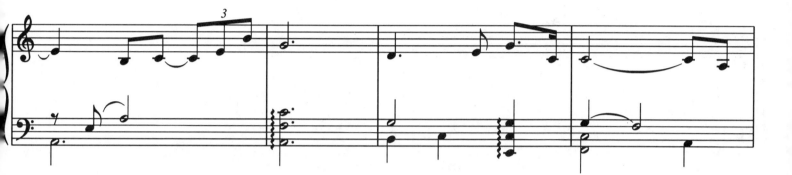

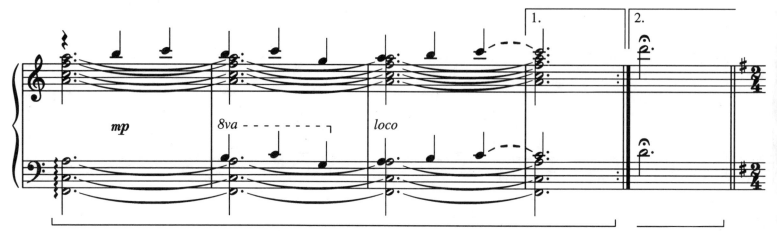

Semplice

Build steadily

pp poco a poco cresc.

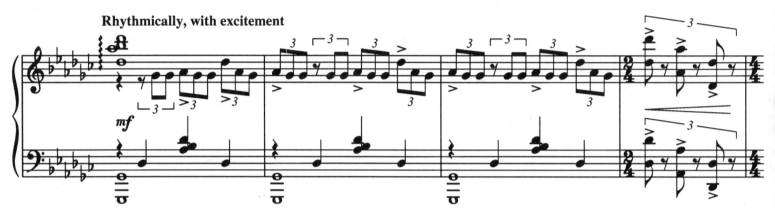

Rhythmically, with excitement

mf

f

Semplice

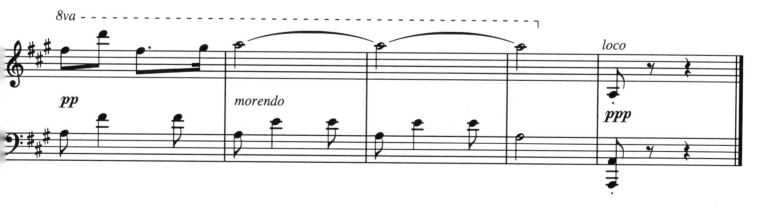

THE GLORY OF LOVE

from GUESS WHO'S COMING TO DINNER
featured in the Motion Picture BEACHES

Words and Music by BILLY HILL

A HARD DAY'S NIGHT
from A HARD DAY'S NIGHT

Words and Music by JOHN LENNON
and PAUL McCARTNEY

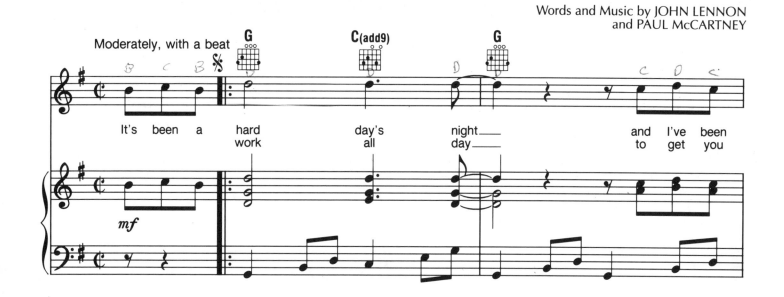

It's been a hard day's night____ and I've been
work all day____ to get you

work-ing like a dog.____ It's been a hard day's night____
mon-ey to buy you things.____ And it's worth it just to hear you say____

____ I should be sleep-ing like a log.____ But when I
You're gon-na give me ev-'ry-thing.____ So why I

ev - 'ry - thing seems to be al - right. When I'm home

feel - ing you hold - ing me tight, tight, yeah, It's been a

You know I feel al - right, You know I

feel al - right.

HEART AND SOUL
from the Paramount Short Subject A SONG IS BORN

Words by FRANK LOESSER
Music by HOAGY CARMICHAEL

HOW DEEP IS YOUR LOVE

from the Motion Picture SATURDAY NIGHT FEVER

Words and Music by BARRY GIBB,
MAURICE GIBB and ROBIN GIBB

feel you in my arms a-gain.___ And you come___ to me___ on a sum-
sav - ior when I fall.___ And you may___ not think___ I___ care___

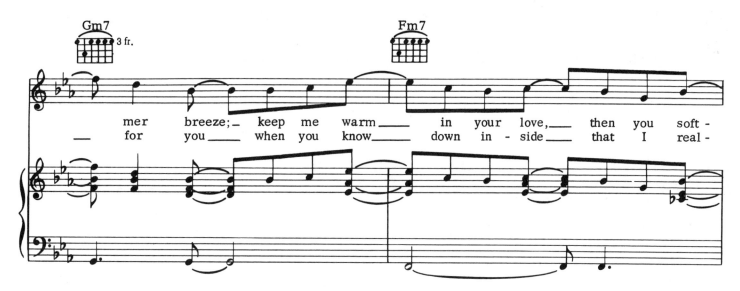

mer breeze;___ keep me warm____ in your love,___ then you soft -
___ for you____ when you know____ down in - side___ that I real -

how deep is your love.

ly leave.___⎱ And it's me you need___ to show:____
ly do.____⎰

How deep___

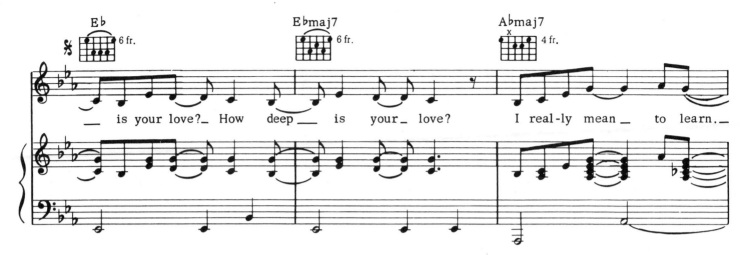

is your love?_ How deep _ is your_ love? I real-ly mean _ to learn._

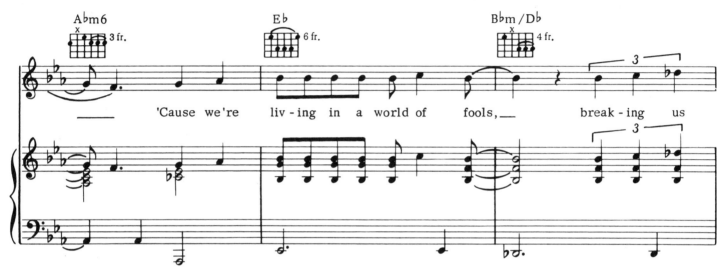

_ 'Cause we're liv-ing in a world of fools,_ break-ing us

down when they all_ should let us be._ We be-long

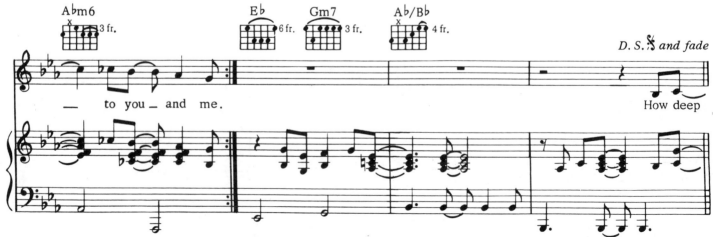

_ to you _ and me.

D. S. 𝄋 and fade

How deep

I HEAR MUSIC
from the Paramount Picture DANCING ON A DIME

Words by FRANK LOESSER
Music by BURTON LANE

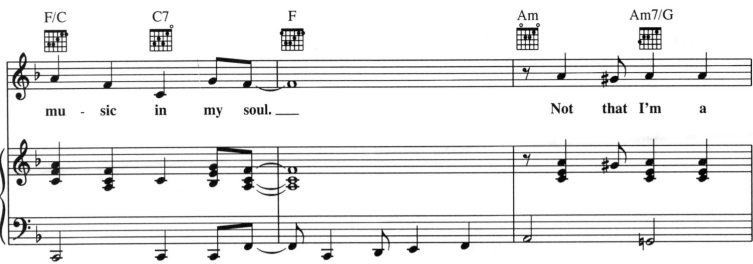

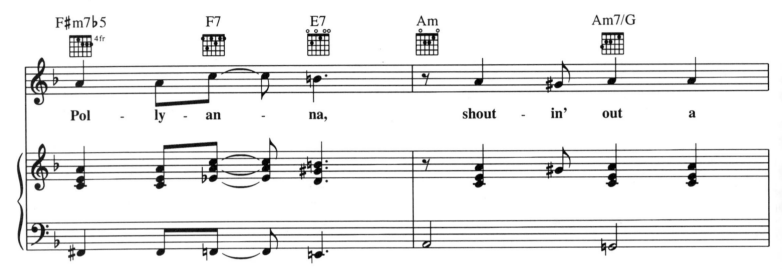

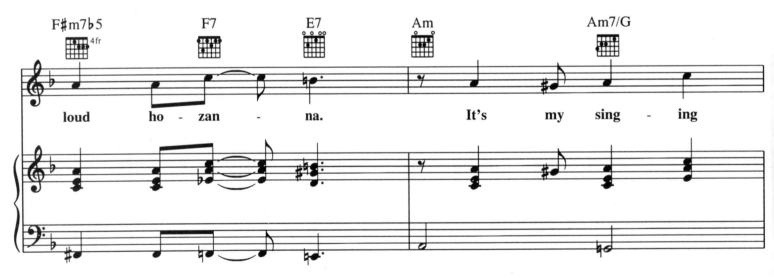

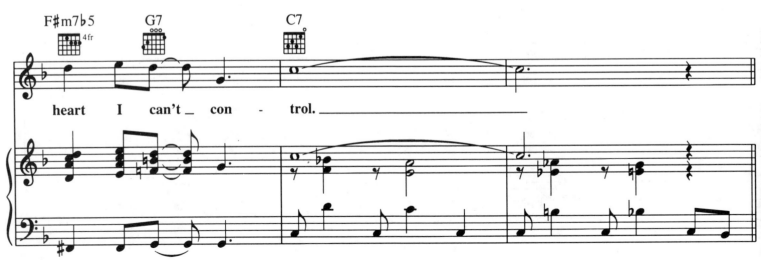

sing-ing of a spar-row in the sky, __ the perk-ing of the cof-fee
right near-by. __ There's my fa-v'rite

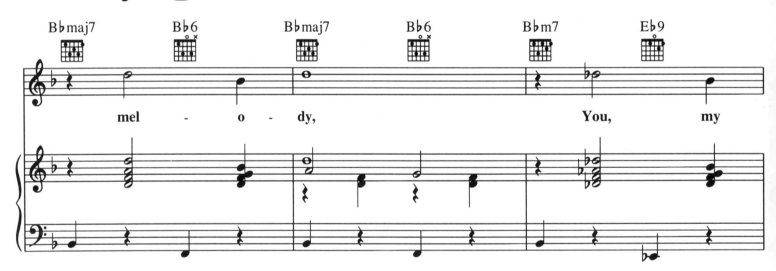

mel-o-dy, You, my

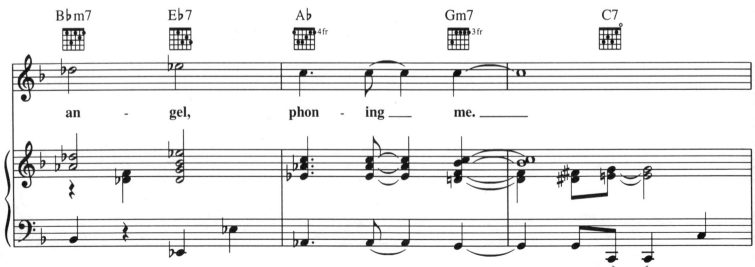

an-gel, phon-ing __ me. _____

I WILL WAIT FOR YOU
from THE UMBRELLAS OF CHERBOURG

Music by MICHEL LEGRAND
Original French Text by JACQUES DEMY
English Lyrics by NORMAN GIMBEL

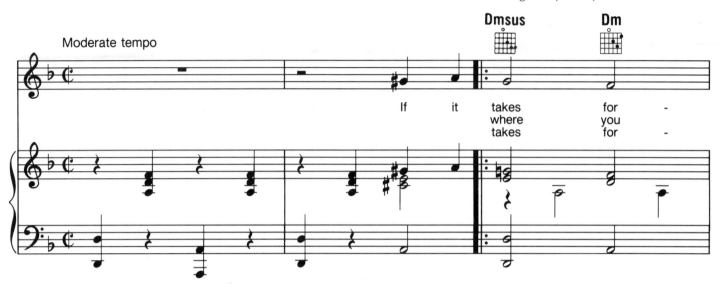

Moderate tempo

If it takes for -
where you
takes for -

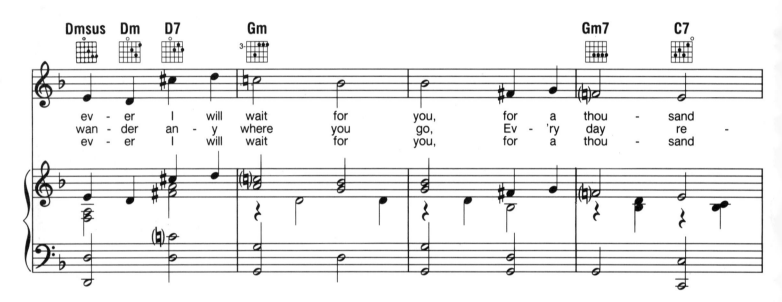

ev - er I will wait for you, for a thou - sand
wan - der an - y where you go, Ev - 'ry day re -
ev - er I will wait for you, for a thou - sand

sum - mers I will wait for you, 'Til you're back be -
mem - ber how I love you so, In your heart be -
sum - mers I will wait for you, 'Til you're back be

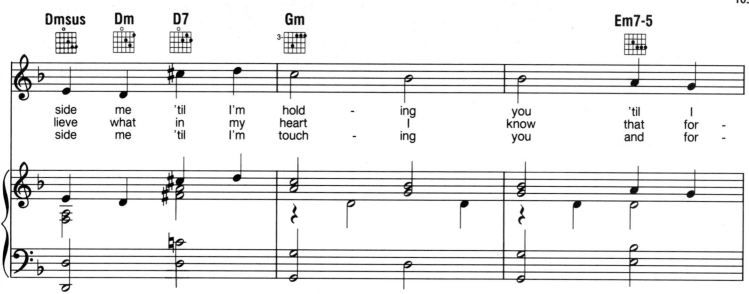

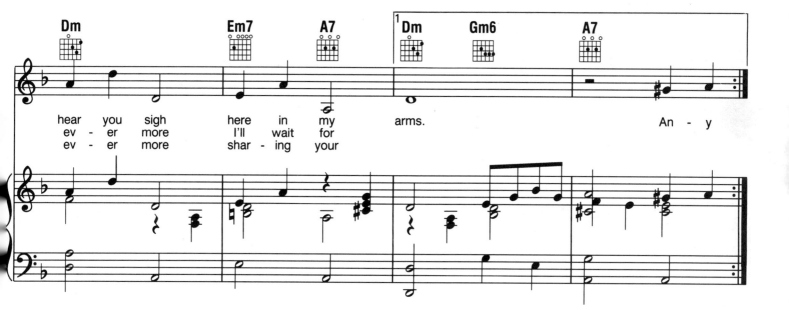

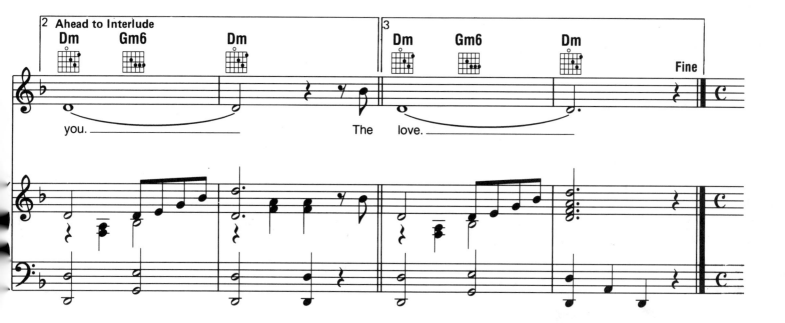

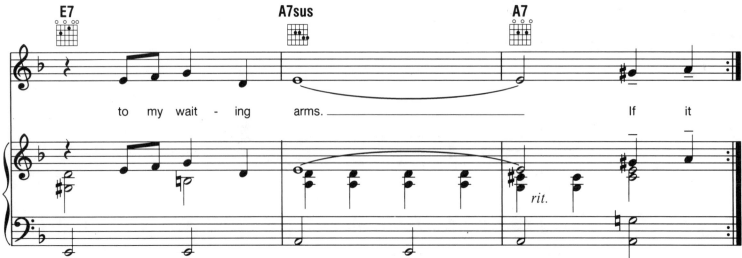

I'M EASY
from NASHVILLE

Words and Music by
KEITH CARRADINE

It's not my way to love you just when no-one's look-ing. It's not my way to take your hand if I'm not sure. It's not my way to let you see what's go-ing on in-side of me; when it's a love you won't be need-ing, you're not free. Please stop

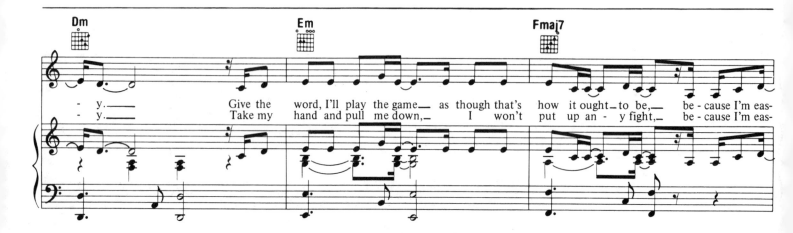

I'M OLD FASHIONED
from YOU WERE NEVER LOVELIER

Words by JOHNNY MERCER
Music by JEROME KERN

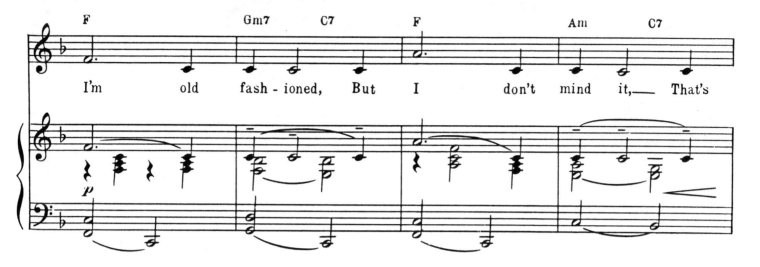

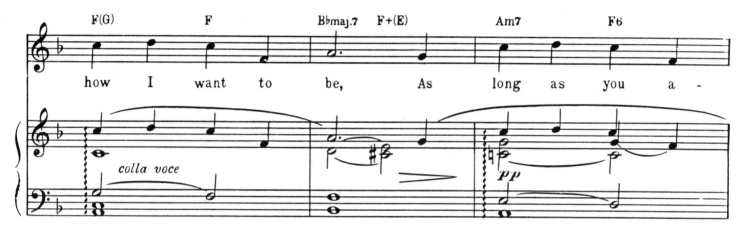

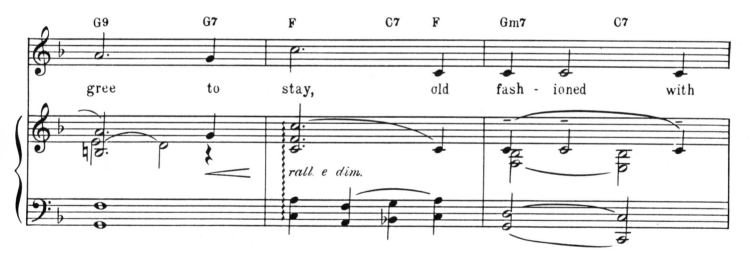

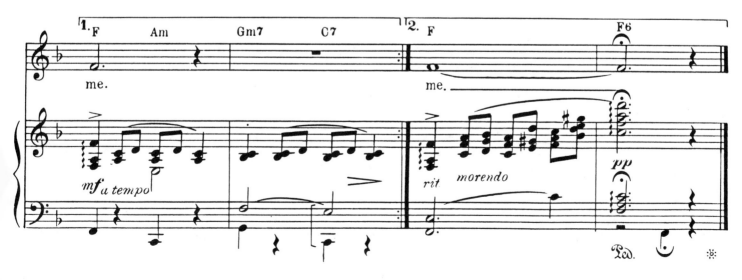

ISN'T IT ROMANTIC?

from the Paramount Picture LOVE ME TONIGHT

Words by LORENZ HART
Music by RICHARD RODGERS

IT'S EASY TO REMEMBER
from the Paramount Picture MISSISSIPPI

Words by LORENZ HART
Music by RICHARD RODGERS

IT COULD HAPPEN TO YOU

from the Paramount Picture AND THE ANGELS SING

Words by JOHNNY BURKE
Music by JAMES VAN HEUSEN

IT MIGHT AS WELL BE SPRING
from STATE FAIR

Lyrics by OSCAR HAMMERSTEIN II
Music by RICHARD RODGERS

IT'S A GRAND NIGHT FOR SINGING
from STATE FAIR

Lyrics by OSCAR HAMMERSTEIN II
Music by RICHARD RODGERS

It's a grand night for sing - ing! The moon is

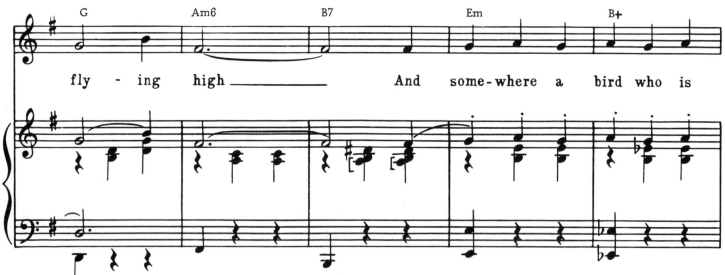

fly - ing high _____ And some-where a bird who is

bound he'll be heard, Is throw-ing his heart at the sky.

It's a grand night for sing - ing! The

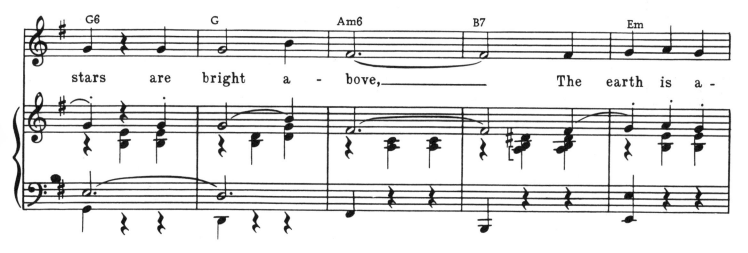

stars are bright a - bove,_____ The earth is a-

glow and to add to the show, I think I am fall-ing in

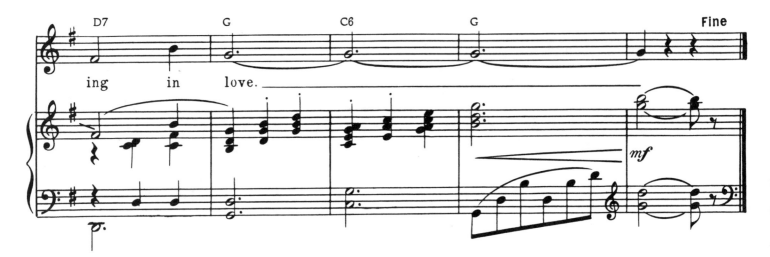

THE LAST TIME I SAW PARIS
from LADY, BE GOOD

Lyrics by OSCAR HAMMERSTEIN II
Music by JEROME KERN

134

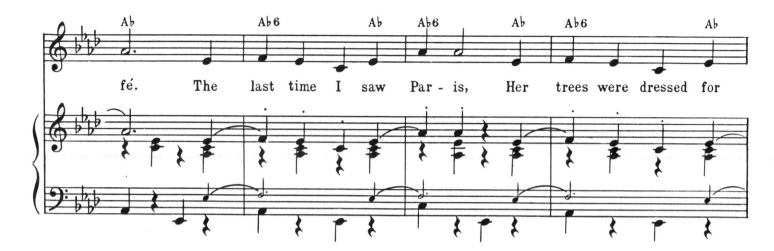

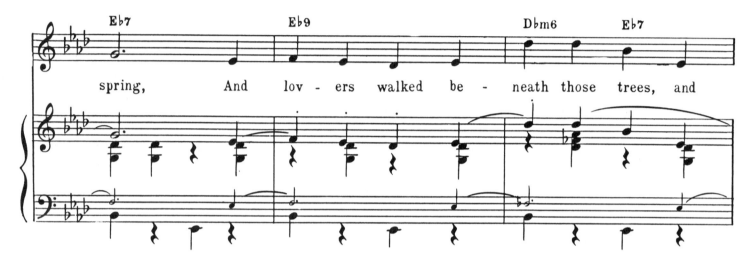

squeak-y horns was mu-sic to my ears. The last time I saw

Par-is, Her heart was warm and gay. No mat-ter how they

change her, I'll re-mem-ber her ____ that way.

2. I'll way. ____

LET'S HEAR IT FOR THE BOY

from the Paramount Motion Picture FOOTLOOSE

Words by DEAN PITCHFORD
Music by TOM SNOW

LONG AGO
(And Far Away)
from COVER GIRL

Words by IRA GERSHWIN
Music by JEROME KERN

Moderately

Con moto

Drear-y days are o-ver. Life's a four-leaf clo-ver.

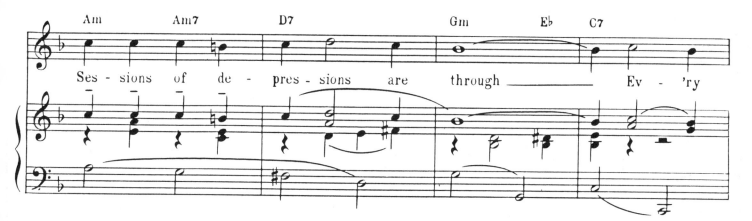

Ses-sions of de-pres-sions are through _____ Ev-'ry

hope I longed for long a-go, comes true. _____

Refrain *(cantabile)*

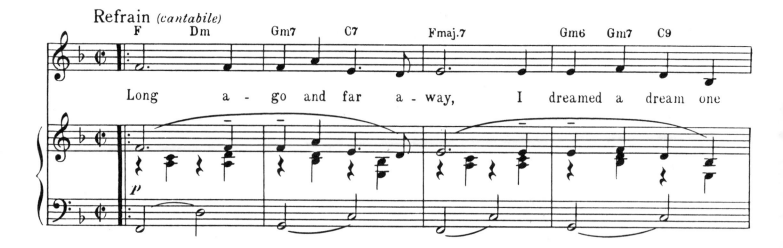

Long a - go and far a - way, I dreamed a dream one

day And now that dream is here be - side me.

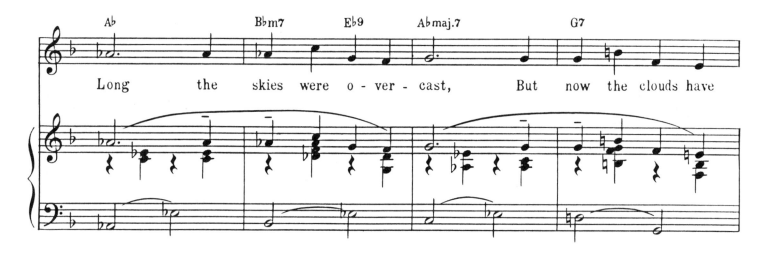

Long the skies were o - ver - cast, But now the clouds have

passed: You're here at last! _____ Chills run

LOUISE
from the Paramount Picture INNOCENTS OF PARIS

Words by LEO ROBIN
Music by RICHARD A. WHITING

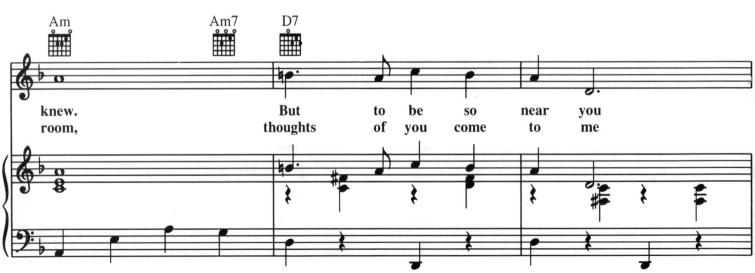

LOVE LETTERS
Theme from the Paramount Picture LOVE LETTERS

Words by EDWARD HEYMAN
Music by VICTOR YOUNG

LOVE ME TENDER

from LOVE ME TENDER

Words and Music by ELVIS PRESLEY
and VERA MATSON

Moderately slow

Verse

1. Love Me Ten - der, love me sweet;
2. Love Me Ten - der, love me long;
3. Love Me Ten - der, love me dear;

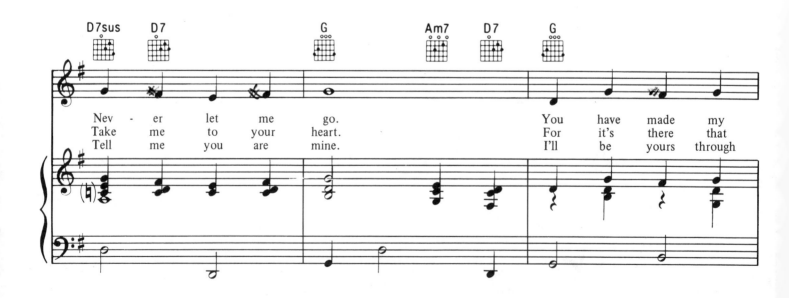

Nev - er let me go. You have made my
Take me to your heart. For it's made there that
Tell me you are mine. I'll be there yours through

EXTRA VERSE   4. When at last my dreams come true,
Darling, this I know:
Happiness will follow you
Everywhere you go.

MIMI
from the Paramount Picture LOVE ME TONIGHT

Words by LORENZ HART
Music by RICHARD RODGERS

Mi-mi, You've got me sad and dream-y,

You could free me, If you'd see me, Mi-mi,

You know I'd like to have a lit-tle son of a Mi-mi bye and

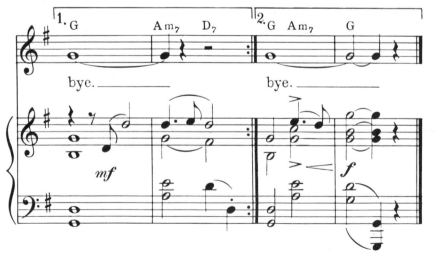

bye. bye.

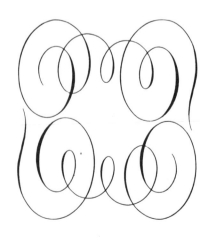

MONA LISA
from the Paramount Picture CAPTAIN CAREY, U.S.A.

By JAY LIVINGSTON
and RAY EVANS

Refrain Slowly Rubato

Mo - na Li - sa, Mo - na Li - sa men have named you: You're so

like the la - dy with the mys-tic smile. Is it on-ly 'cause you're lone-ly_ they have

blamed you for that Mo - na Li - sa strange-ness in your smile? Do you

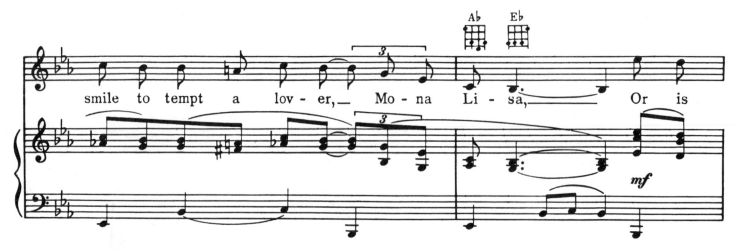

smile to tempt a lov - er,_ Mo - na Li - sa,_ Or is

this your way to hide a brok-en heart? Man-y dreams have been brought to your

door-step. They just lie there, and they die there. Are you

warm, are you real, Mo - na Li - sa, Or just a

cold and lone-ly, love-ly work of art? Mo - na art?

MOON RIVER
from the Paramount Picture BREAKFAST AT TIFFANY'S

Words by JOHNNY MERCER
Music by HENRY MANCINI

ON GOLDEN POND
Main Theme from ON GOLDEN POND

Music by
DAVE GRUSIN

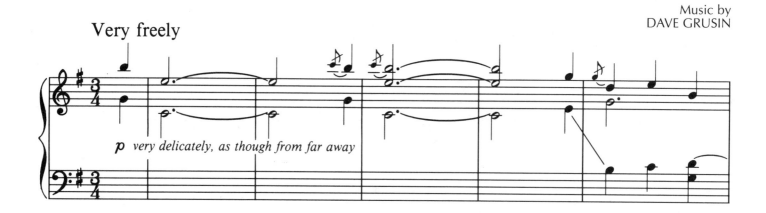

Very freely

p very delicately, as though from far away

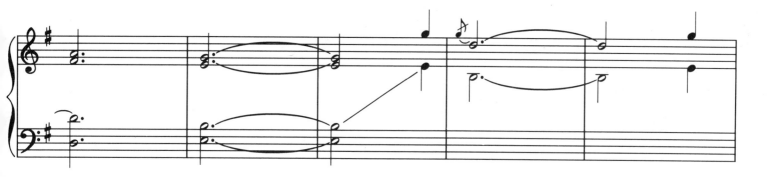

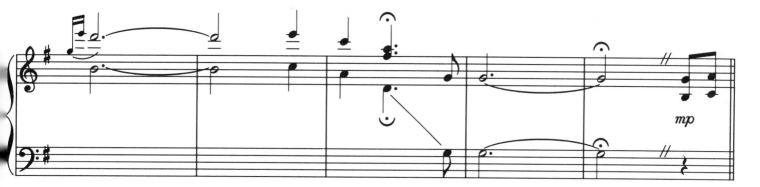

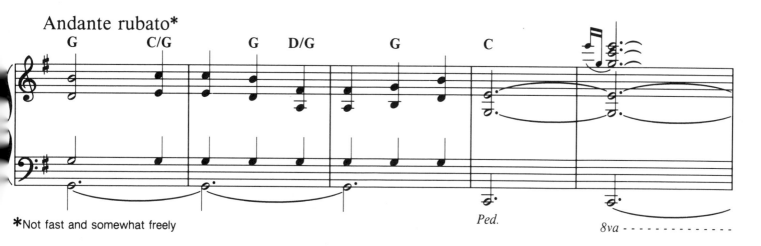

Andante rubato*

G   C/G   G   D/G   G   C

*Not fast and somewhat freely

Ped.

8va - - - - - - - - - - - - - - -

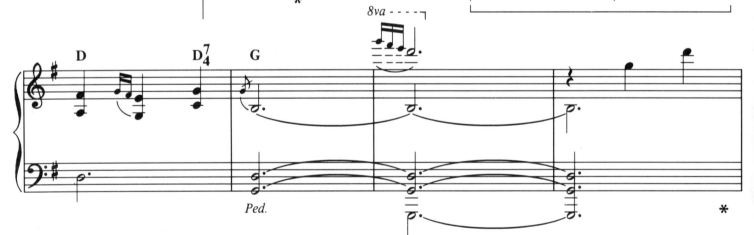

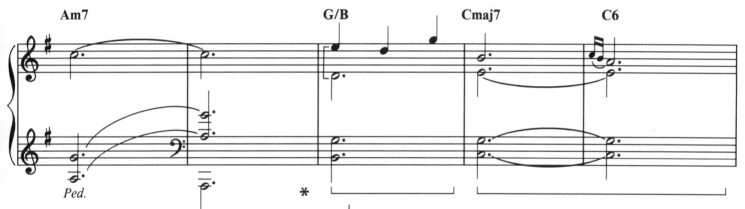

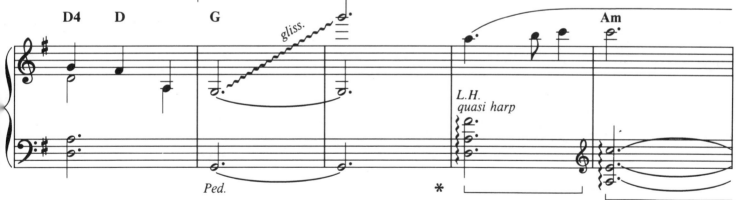

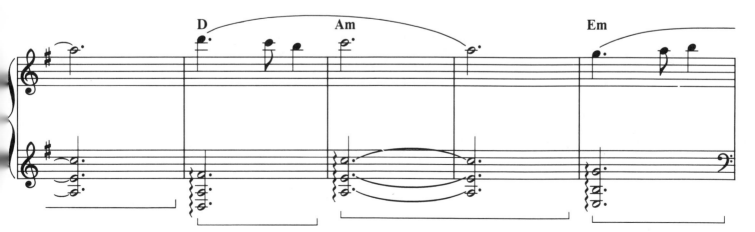

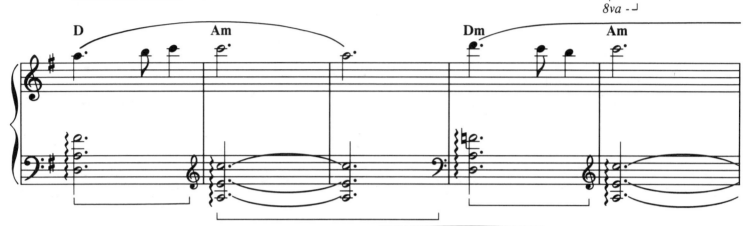

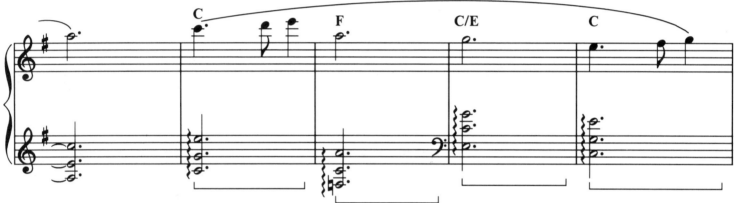

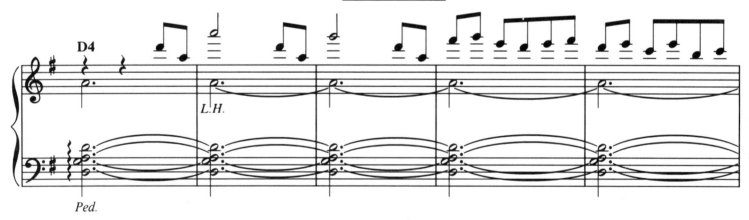

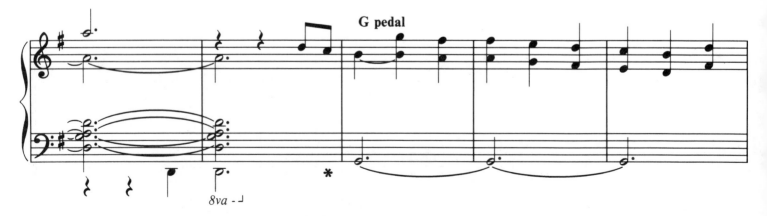

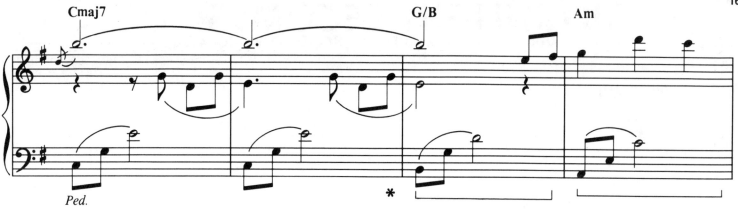

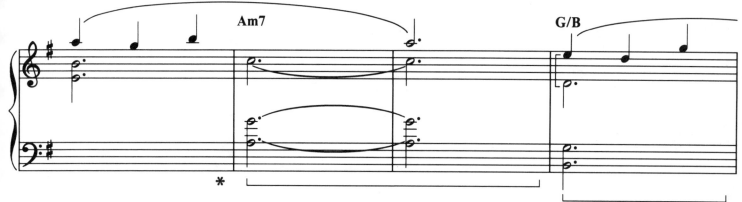

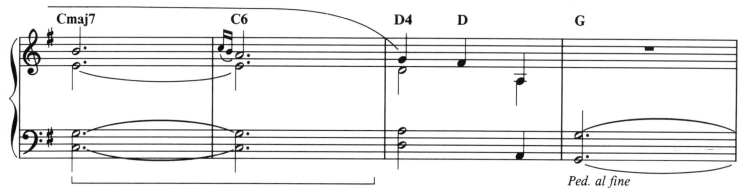

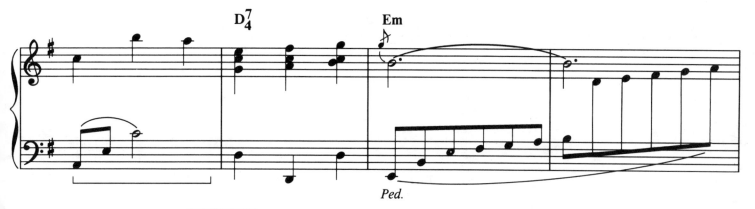

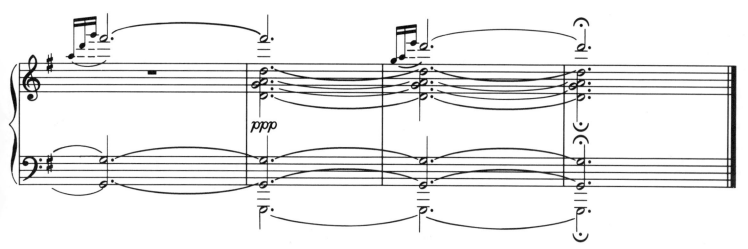

MOONLIGHT BECOMES YOU
from the Paramount Picture ROAD TO MOROCCO

Words by JOHNNY BURKE
Music by JAMES VAN HEUSEN

THE MUSIC OF GOODBYE
Love Theme from OUT OF AFRICA

Words by ALAN and MARILYN BERGMAN
Music by JOHN BARRY

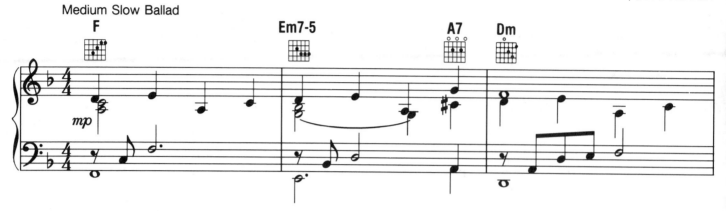

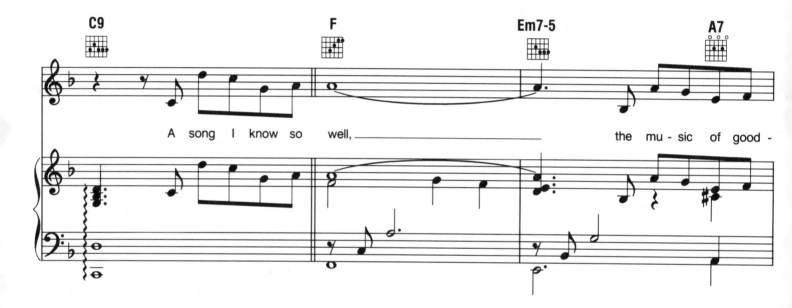

A song I know so well, _____ the mu-sic of good-

bye a-gain. _____ It's there each time we say "hel-lo." _____

MCA music publishing

THE ODD COUPLE
Theme from the Paramount Picture THE ODD COUPLE

Words by SAMMY CAHN
Music by NEAL HEFTI

ONE TIN SOLDIER

from BILLY JACK

Words and Music by DENNIS LAMBERT
and BRIAN POTTER

Moderately slow rock tempo

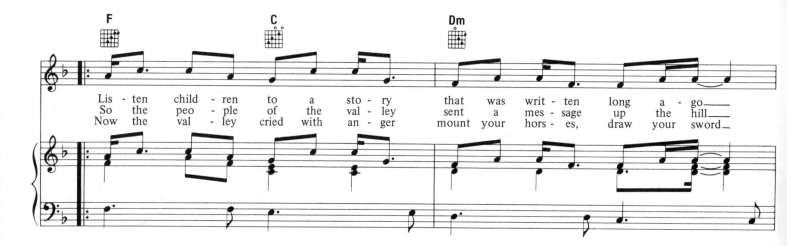

Lis - ten child - ren to a sto - ry that was writ - ten long a - go___
So the peo - ple of the val - ley sent a mes - sage up the hill___
Now the val - ley cried with an - ger mount your hors - es, draw your sword___

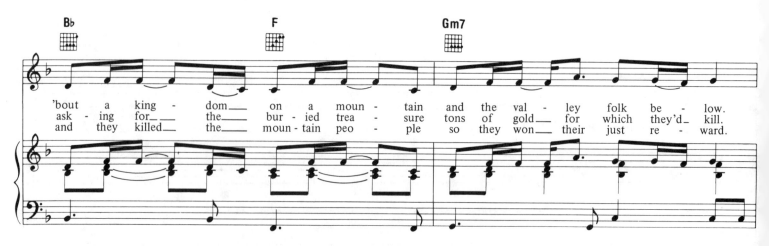

'bout a king - dom___ on a moun - tain and the val - ley folk be - low.
ask - ing for___ the___ bur - ied trea - sure tons of gold___ for which they'd_ kill.
and they killed___ the___ moun - tain peo - ple so they won___ their just re - ward.

MCA music publishing

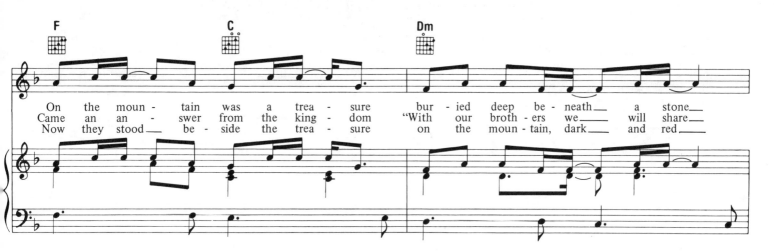

On the moun - tain was a trea - sure bur - ied deep be - neath a stone
Came an an - swer from the king - dom "With our broth - ers we will share
Now they stood be - side the trea - sure on the moun - tain, dark and red

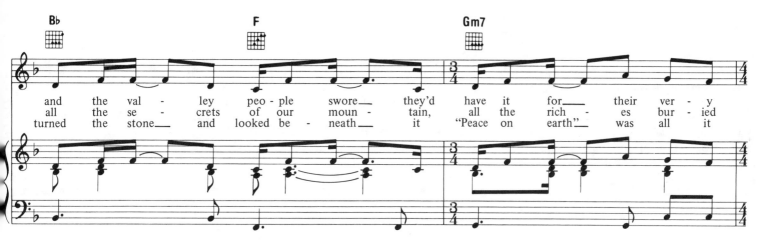

and the val - ley peo - ple swore they'd have it for their ver - y
all the se - crets of our moun - tain, all the rich - es bur - ied
turned the stone and looked be - neath it "Peace on earth" was all it

own.
there." Go a - head and hate your neigh - bor,
said.

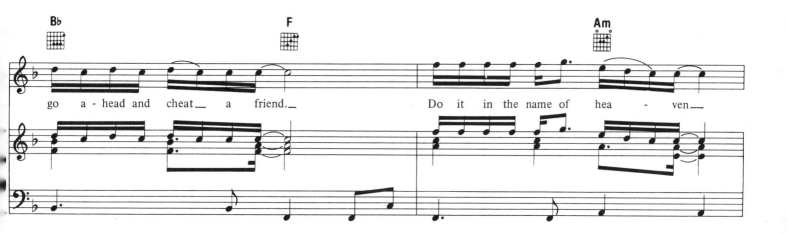

go a - head and cheat a friend. Do it in the name of hea - ven

Jus - ti - fy it in the end.___ There won't be an - y trum - pets blow - in'___

come the judge - ment day on the blood - y morn - ing af - ter___

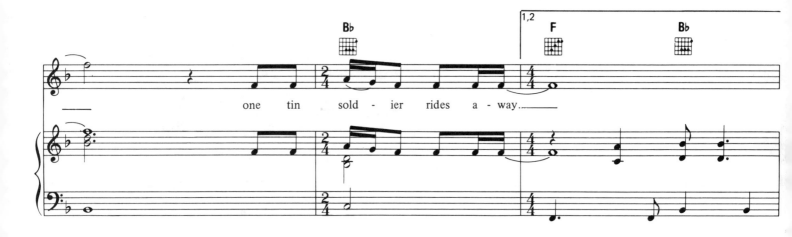

one tin sold - ier rides a - way.___

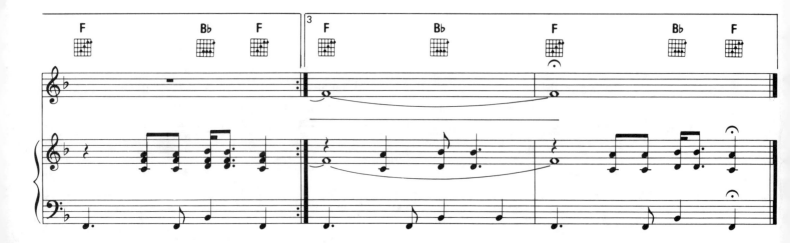

THE RAINBOW CONNECTION

from THE MUPPET MOVIE

By PAUL WILLIAMS and
KENNETH L. ASCHER

Why are there so man-y songs a - bout rain - bows, and
Who said that ev - 'ry wish would be heard and an - swered and

what's on the oth - er side? _____
wished on the morn - ing star? _____

Rain - bows are vis - ions, ___ but on - ly il - lu - sions, And
Some - bod - y thought of that, and some - one be - lieved it;

184

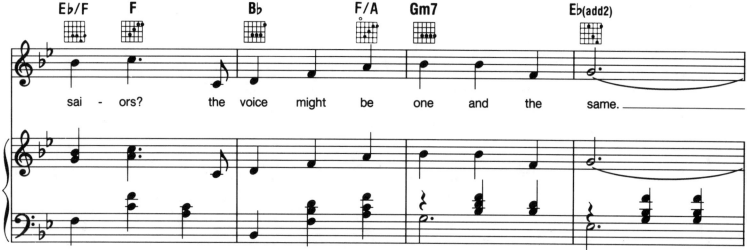

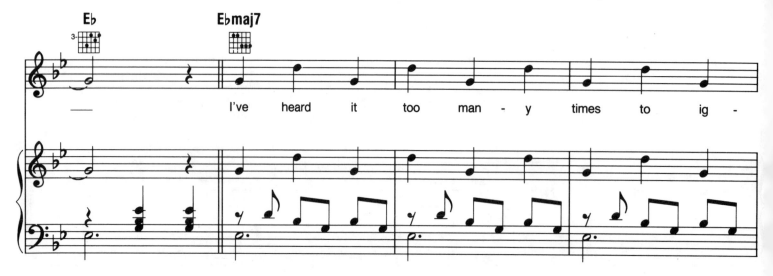

QUE SERA, SERA
(Whatever Will Be, Will Be)
from THE MAN WHO KNEW TOO MUCH

Words and Music by
JAY LIVINGSTON
and RAY EVANS

When I was just just a lit - tle
just a child in

{girl} {boy} I asked my moth - er, "What will I
school, I asked my teach - er, "What should I

be?_____ Will I be {pret - ty?}
{hand - some?}
try?_____ Should I be paint pic - tures?

MCA music publishing

Will I be rich?" Here's what she said to
Should I be sing rich?" This what was her wise re-

me:⟩ "Que se - ra, se - ra,_____ What-
ply:⟩

ev - er will be will be;_____ The

fu - ture's not ours to see. Que se -

RAIDERS MARCH

from the Paramount Motion Picture RAIDERS OF THE LOST ARK

By JOHN WILLIAMS

March tempo

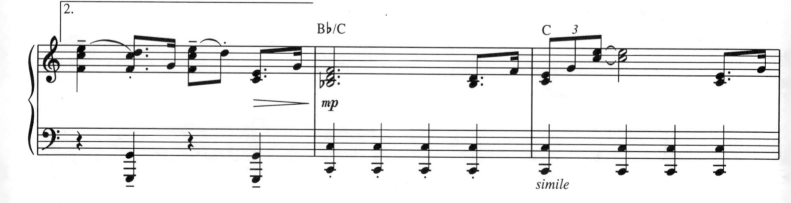

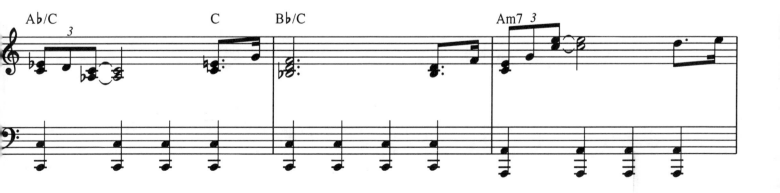

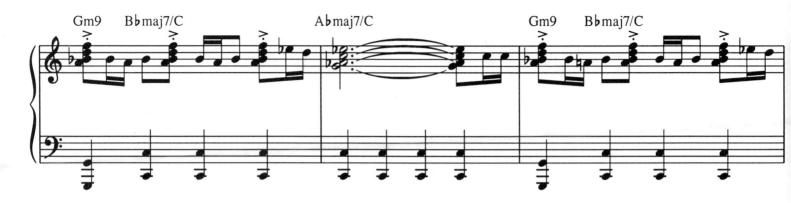

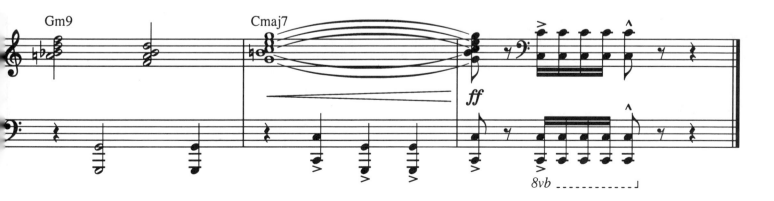

RAINDROPS KEEP FALLIN' ON MY HEAD
from BUTCH CASSIDY AND THE SUNDANCE KID

Lyric by HAL DAVID
Music by BURT BACHARACH

Rain - drops keep fall - in' on my

head, and just like the guy whose feet are too big for his

bed, Noth - in' seems to fit. Those rain - drops are fall - in' on my

soon be turn - in' red. Cry - in's not for me 'cause

I'm nev - er gon - na stop the rain by com-plain-in'. Be - cause I'm

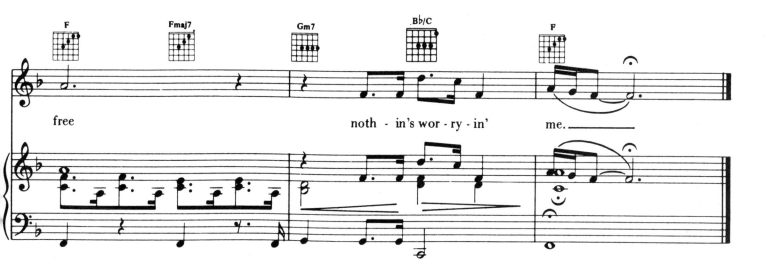

free noth - in's wor - ry - in' me.

SOMEWHERE IN TIME
from SOMEWHERE IN TIME

By JOHN BARRY

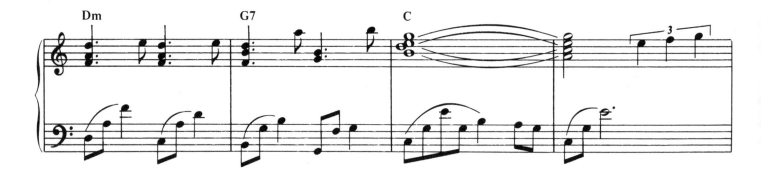

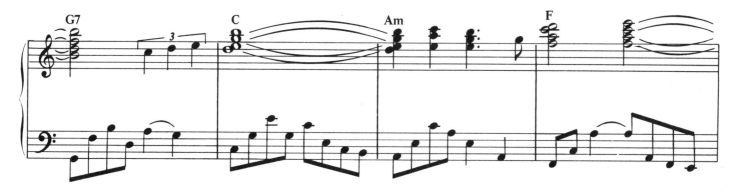

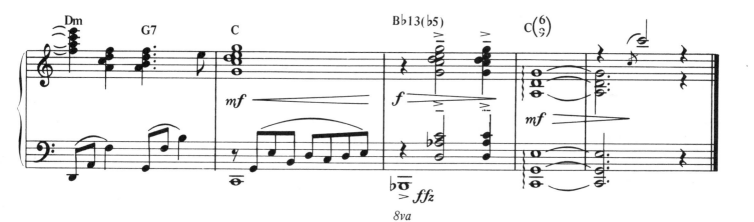

SOMEWHERE OUT THERE

from AN AMERICAN TAIL

By JAMES HORNER,
BARRY MANN and CYNTHIA WEIL

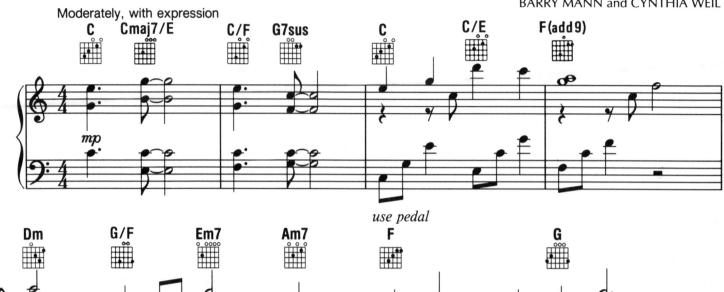

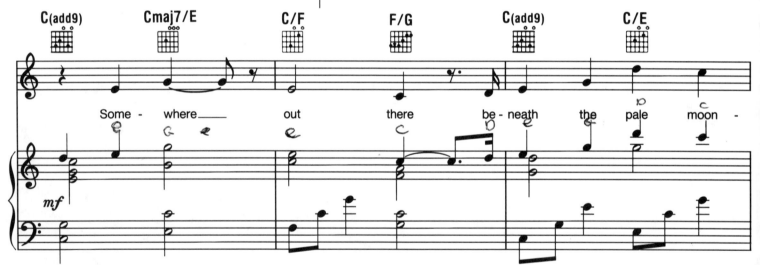

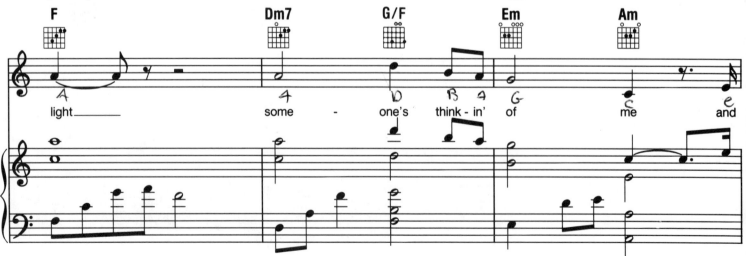

STAR TREK® - THE MOTION PICTURE

Theme from the Paramount Picture STAR TREK: THE MOTION PICTURE

Music by JERRY GOLDSMITH

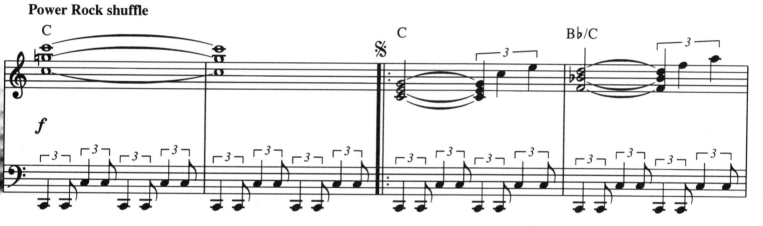

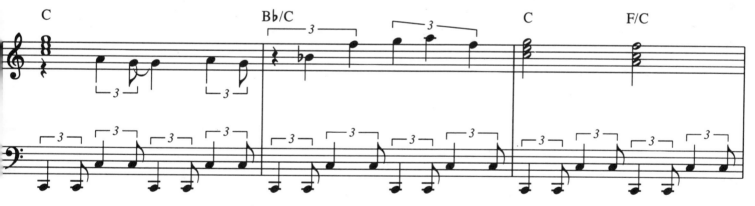

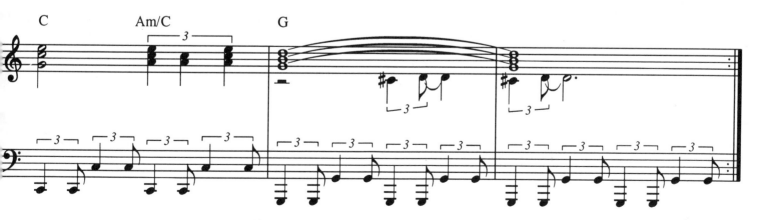

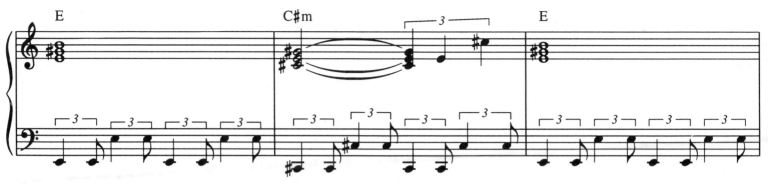

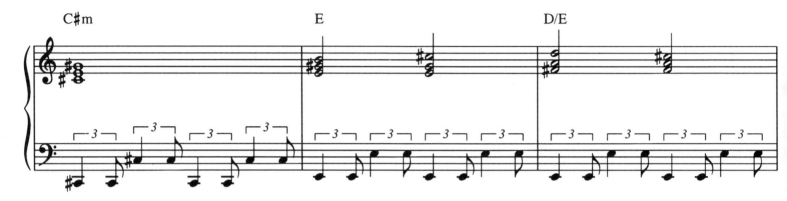

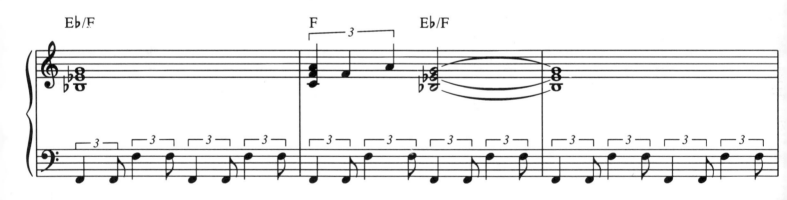

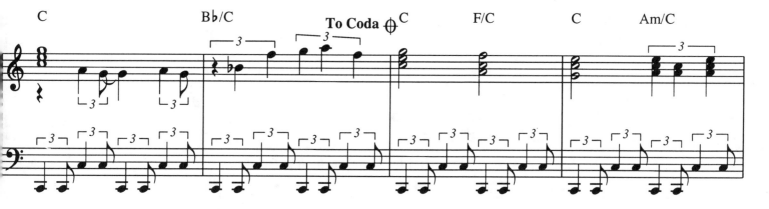

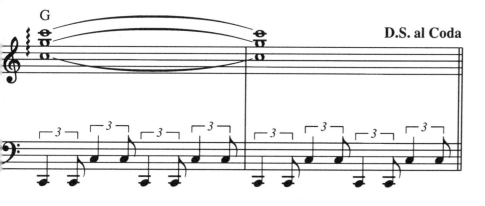

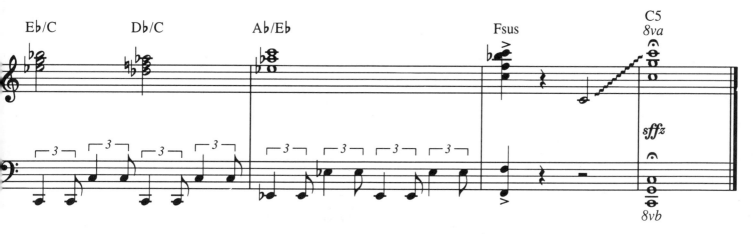

SPEAK SOFTLY, LOVE
(Love Theme)
from the Paramount Picture THE GODFATHER

Words by LARRY KUSIK
Music by NINO ROTA

TAKE MY BREATH AWAY
(Love Theme)
from the Paramount Picture TOP GUN

Words and Music by GIORGIO MORODER
and TOM WHITLOCK

Lyrics:

Watch-ing ev-'ry mo-tion in ___
Watch-ing, I keep wait-ing, still ___
Watch-ing ev-'ry mo-tion in ___

___ my fool-ish lov-er's game; ___
___ an-tic-i-pat-ing love, ___
___ this fool-ish lov-er's game; ___

on this end-less o-cean, fi-
nev-er hes-i-tat-ing to
haunt-ed by the no-tion some-

A TIME FOR US
(Love Theme)
from the Paramount Picture ROMEO AND JULIET

Words by LARRY KUSIK and EDDIE SNYDER
Music by NINO ROTA

THEME FROM
"TERMS OF ENDEARMENT"

from the Paramount Picture TERMS OF ENDEARMENT

By MICHAEL GORE

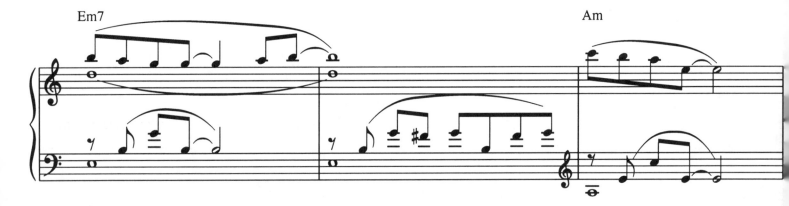

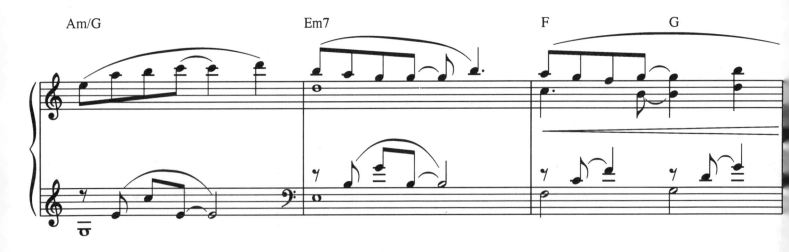

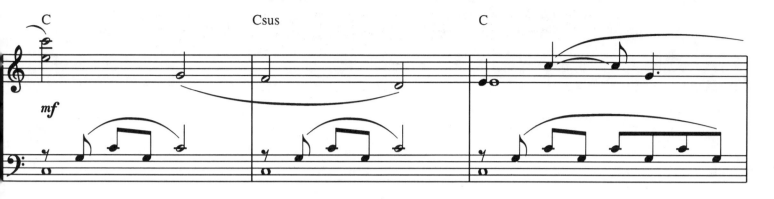

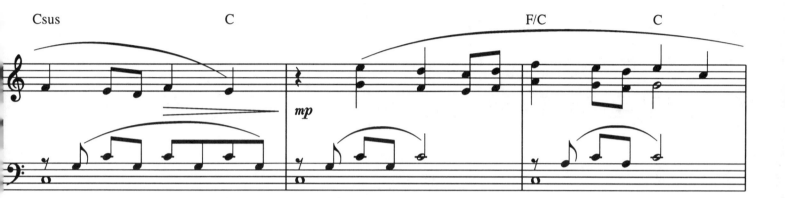

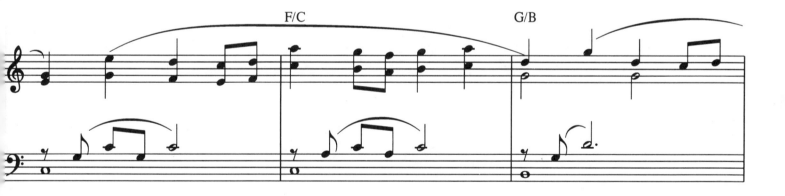

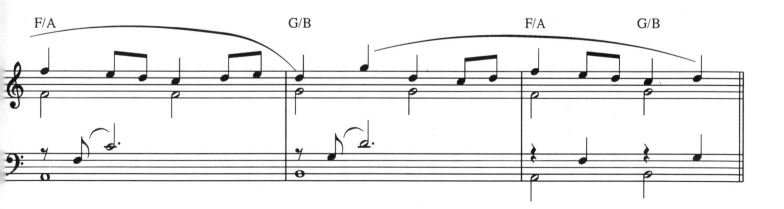

222

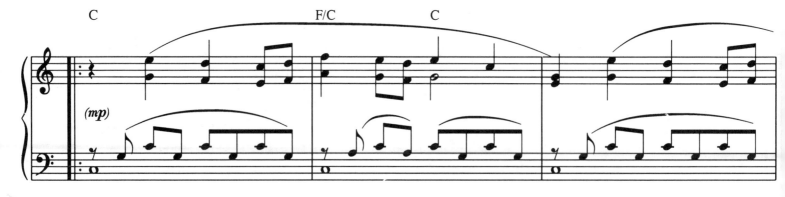

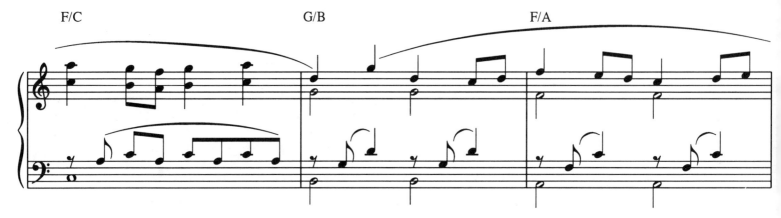

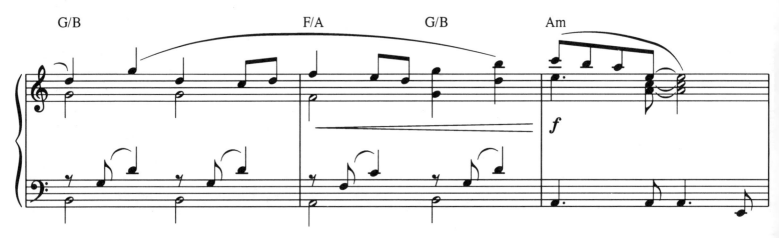

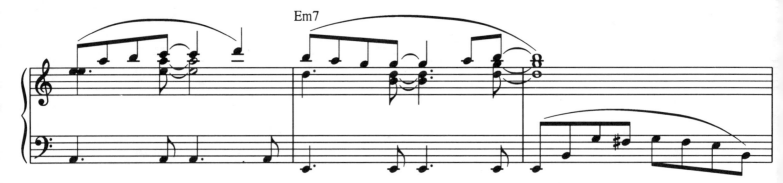

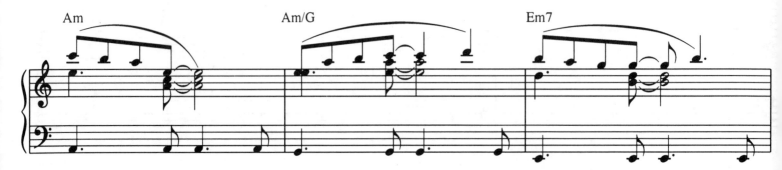

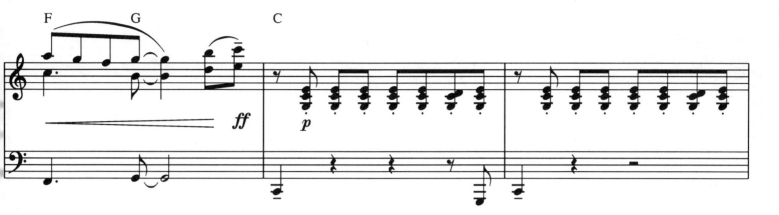

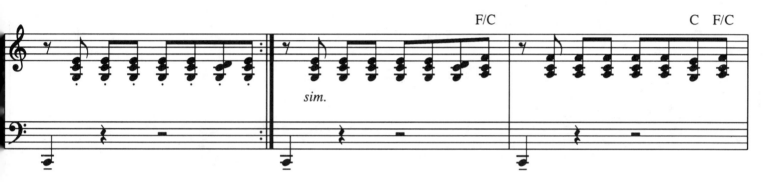

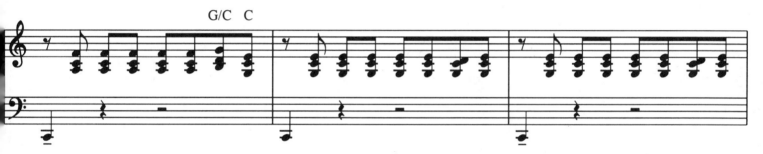

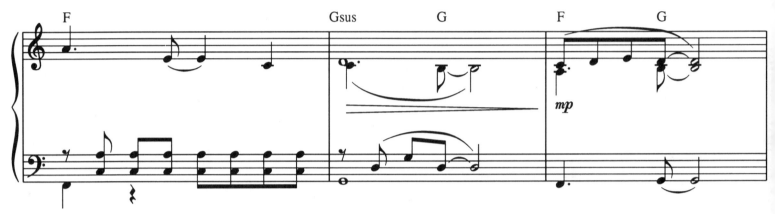

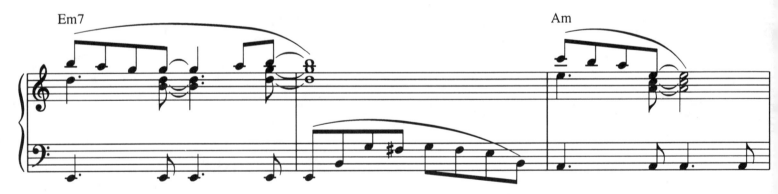

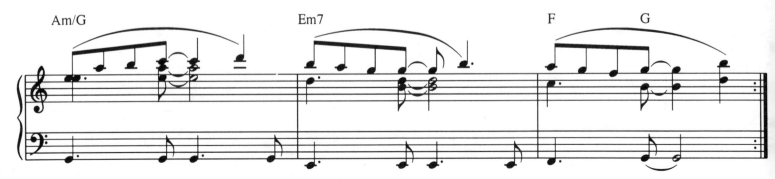

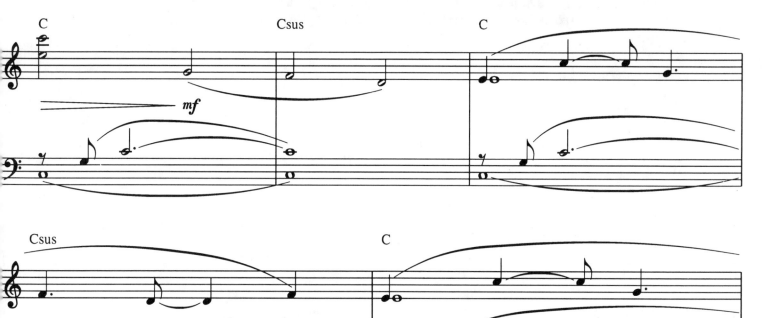

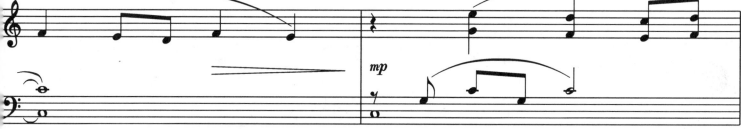

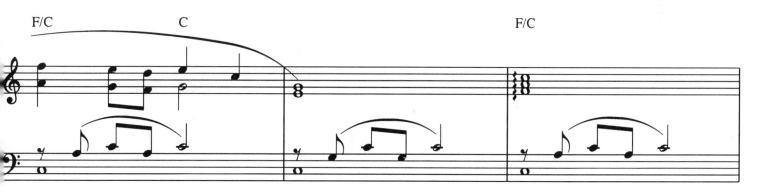

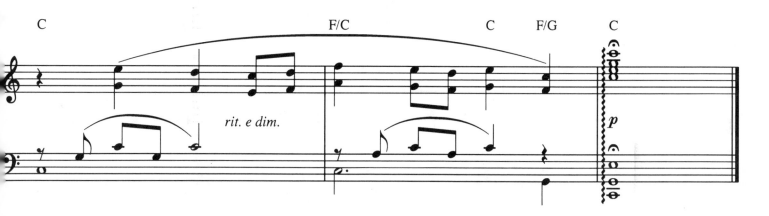

THANKS FOR THE MEMORY

from the Paramount Picture BIG BROADCAST OF 1938

Words and Music by LEO ROBIN
and RALPH RAINGER

THAT OLD BLACK MAGIC

from the Paramount Picture STAR SPANGLED RHYTHM

Words by JOHNNY MERCER
Music by HAROLD ARLEN

UNCHAINED MELODY

from the Motion Picture UNCHAINED
featured in the Motion Picture GHOST

Lyric by HY ZARET
Music by ALEX NORTH

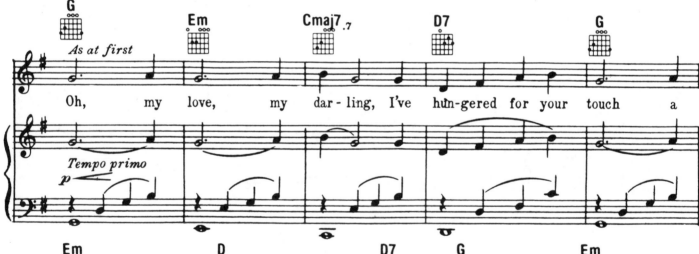

UP WHERE WE BELONG

from the Paramount Picture AN OFFICER AND A GENTLEMAN

Words by WILL JENNINGS
Music by BUFFY SAINTE-MARIE and JACK NITZSCHE

Who knows what to - mor-row brings;___ in a
Some hang on to "used to be,"___ live their

world, few hearts sur - vive? All I know is the
lives look - ing be - hind. All we have is

way I feel;___ when it's real, I keep it a - live.___ The
here and now;___ all our life, out there to find.___

THE WAY YOU LOOK TONIGHT
from SWING TIME

Words by DOROTHY FIELDS
Music by JEROME KERN

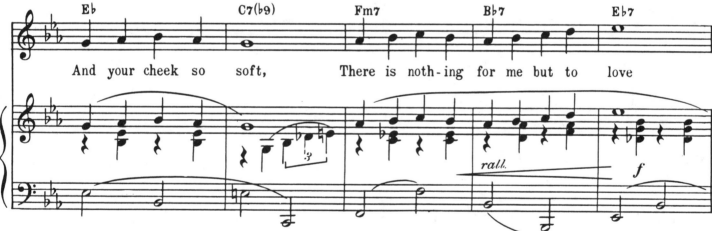

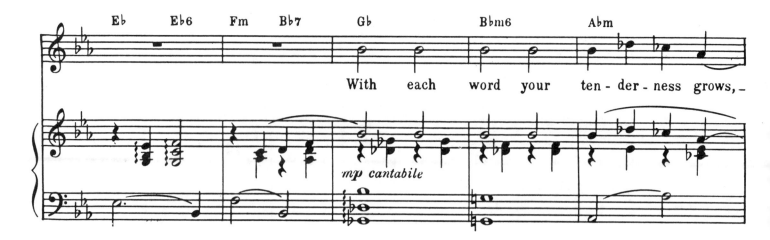

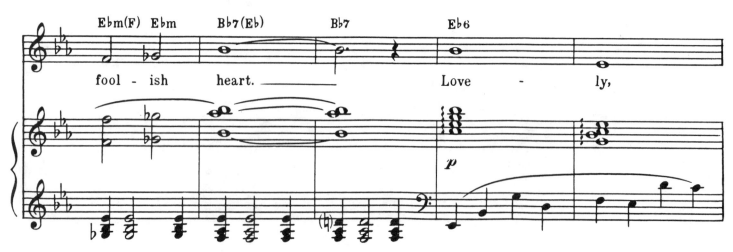

nev-er, nev-er change, Keep that breath-less charm, Won't you please ar-

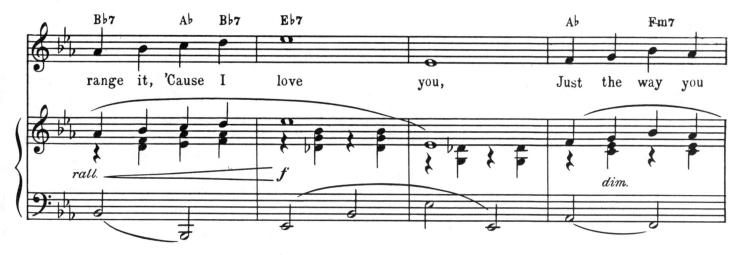

range it, 'Cause I love you, Just the way you

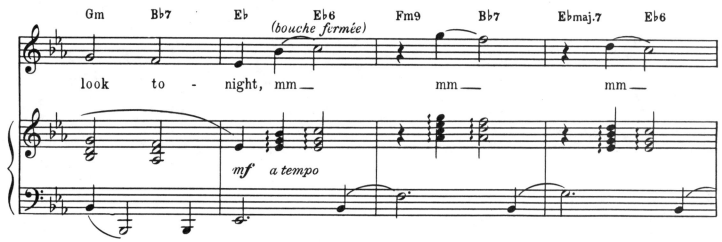

look to-night, mm___ mm___ mm___

mm___ Just the way you look to-night.___

WHERE DO I BEGIN
(Love Theme)
from the Paramount Picture LOVE STORY

Words by CARL SIGMAN
Music by FRANCIS LAI

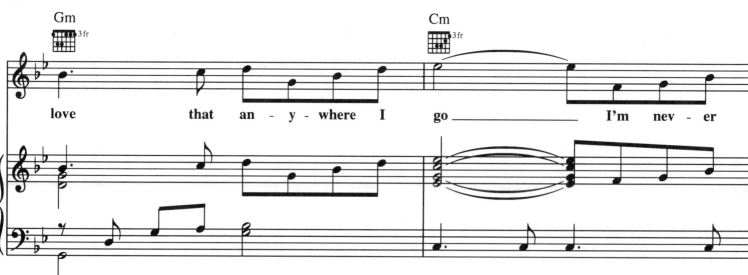

love that an-y-where I go _____ I'm nev-er

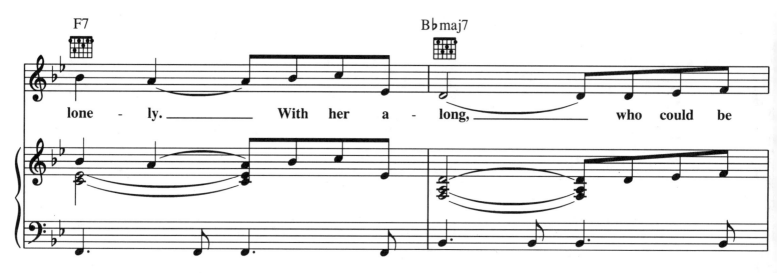

lone-ly. _____ With her a-long, _____ who could be

lone-ly? _____ I reach for her hand, _____ it's al-ways there. _____

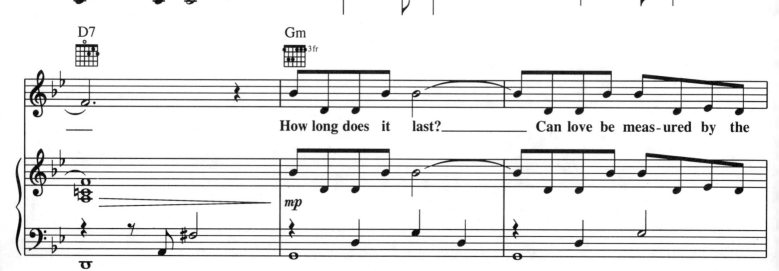

— How long does it last? _____ Can love be meas-ured by the

YELLOW SUBMARINE

from YELLOW SUBMARINE

Words and Music by
JOHN LENNON and PAUL McCARTNEY

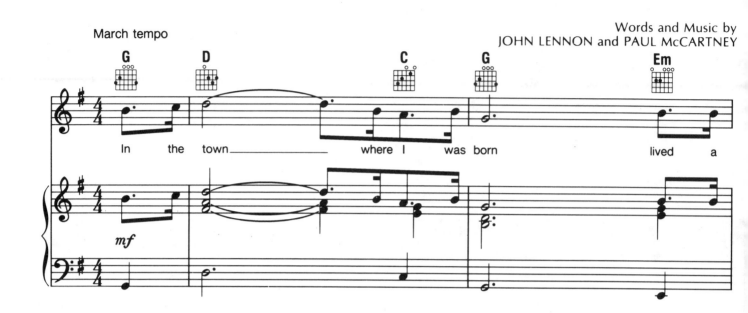

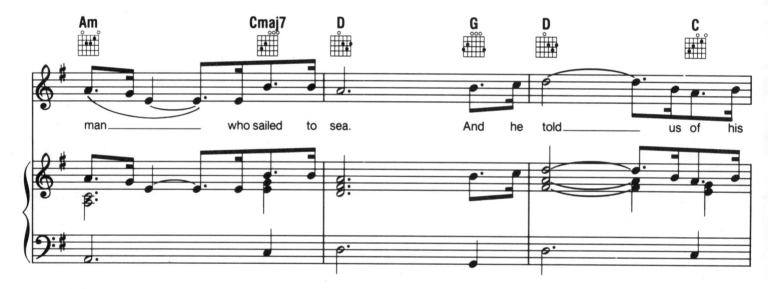

Chorus:

D.S. and Fade

YOU MUST LOVE ME

from the Cinergi Motion Picture EVITA

Lyric by TIM RICE
Music by ANDREW LLOYD WEBBER

Flowing ♩=92

1. Where do we go from here?
2. (See additional lyrics)

This is-n't where we in-tend-ed to be.___ We had it all,___ you be-

lieved ___ in me,___ I be-lieved ___ in you.___

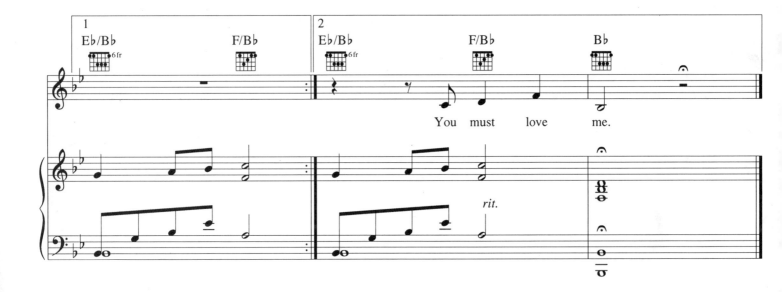

Additional Lyrics

Verse 2: *(Instrumental 8 bars)*
Why are you at my side?
How can I be any use to you now?
Give me a chance and I'll let you see how
Nothing has changed.
Deep in my heart I'm concealing
Things that I'm longing to say,
Scared to confess what I'm feeling
Frightened you'll slip away,
You must love me.

A WHOLE NEW WORLD

from Walt Disney's ALADDIN

Music by ALAN MENKEN
Lyrics by TIM RICE

264

YOU SHOULD BE DANCING

from SATURDAY NIGHT FEVER

Moderately, with a beat

Words and Music by BARRY GIBB,
MAURICE GIBB and ROBIN GIBB

My ba-by moves__ at mid-night,__ goes she
juic-y and __ she's trou-ble,__

right on till the dawn;__ my wom-an takes me high-er,
gets it to me good;__ my wom-an gives me pow-er,

my wom - an keeps__ me warm.__
goes right down to___ my blood.__

What you

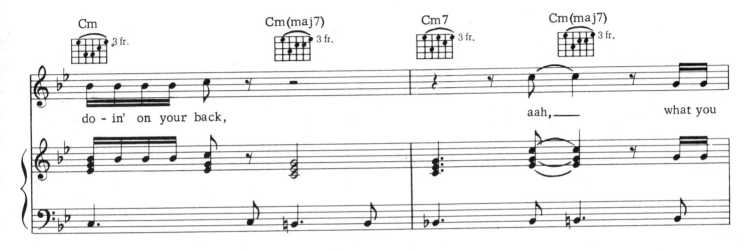

Cm   Cm(maj7)   Cm7   Cm(maj7)

do - in' on your back,   aah, ____   what you

Cm   Cm(maj7)   Cm7   Cm(maj7)   Gm

do-in' on your back,   aah?___ You should be danc - in',__ yeah,__

1.

danc - in',__ yeah.__   She's

More Great Songbooks For Your Collection

All books arranged for piano, voice, and guitar.

ACOUSTIC CLASSICS
32 songs of the 60s and 70s, including: American Pie • Blackbird • Blowin' In The Wind • Bridge Over Troubled Water • Here Comes The Sun • Leaving On A Jet Plane • Still Crazy After All These Years • Vincent (Starry Starry Night) • Where Have All The Flowers Gone? • Your Song • and more.
HLE90000011

ALL YOU NEED IS LOVE
39 songs from the hip years of the late 60s and early 70s, including: All You Need Is Love • Blowin' In The Wind • Born To Be Wild • Bridge Over Troubled Water • Hey Joe • Imagine • Light My Fire • Love Her Madly • Magic Carpet Ride • Mr. Tambourine Man • My Generation • Riders On The Storm • The Sound Of Silence • The Sunshine Of Your Love • Turn! Turn! Turn! • A Whiter Shade Of Pale • and more.
HLE90000044

BIG BOOK OF BROADWAY
64 songs, including: All I Ask of You • Another Suitcase in Another Hall • Any Dream Will Do • Beauty and the Beast • Cabaret • Consider Yourself • Diamonds are a Girl's Best Friend • Edelweiss • Getting to Know You • I Dreamed a Dream • If I Were a Rich Man • The Impossible Dream • Lambeth Walk • Love Changes Everything • Luck be a Lady • Memory • The Music of the Night • Ol' Man River • On My Own • Smoke Gets in Your Eyes • Sun and Moon • Tonight • Unexpected Song • With One Look • and more.
HLE90000154

BIG BOOK OF MOVIE SONGS
66 songs, including: Airport Love Theme • Baby Elephant Walk • Beauty and the Beast • Blue Velvet • Can You Feel the Love Tonight • Chim Chim Cher-ee • A Fine Romance • Forrest Gump Suite • Heart and Soul • Isn't it Romantic? • It Could Happen to You • The Last Time I Saw Paris • Mona Lisa • Moon River • One Tin Soldier • The Rainbow Connection • Somewhere Out There • Star Trek® • Thanks For The Memory • Unchained Melody • A Whole New World • and more.
HLE90000165

THE BIRTH OF ROCK 'N' ROLL
37 songs with historical articles and photos; songs include: All Shook Up • Blue Suede Shoes • Blueberry Hill • Earth Angel • Goodnight, Sweetheart, Goodnight • Long Tall Sally • Rock Around the Clock • Sh-Boom (Life Could Be a Dream) • Tutti Frutti • Whole Lotta Shakin' Goin' On • and more.
HLE90000055

IMAGINE
30 songs for a better world, including: All You Need Is Love • Circle Of Life • Colors Of The Wind • From A Distance • God Help The Outcasts • If I Had A Hammer • Imagine • The Impossible Dream • The Power Of The Dream • Someday • Turn! Turn! Turn! • What The World Needs Now Is Love • With A Little Help From My Friends • and more.
HLE90000033

LOVE IS BLUE
39 songs, including: Angel Eyes • Crazy • Falling in Love Again • I Should Care • I'll Never Smile Again • In a Sentimental Mood • Lush Life • The Man That Got Away • Smoke Gets In Your Eyes • Solitude • The Very Thought of You • You Don't Bring Me Flowers • and more.
HLE90000022

SHAKE, RATTLE, & ROLL
40 songs plus dozens of photos and fun facts about America of the 1950s; songs include: All I Have to Do Is Dream • All Shook Up • Book of Love • Bye Bye Love • Chantilly Lace • Good Golly Miss Molly • Great Balls of Fire • Have I Told You Lately That I Love You • Johnny B. Goode • Lollipop • Long Tall Sally • Maybe Baby • Peggy Sue • Rock Around the Clock • Shake, Rattle and Roll • Splish Splash • That'll Be the Day • Unchained Melody • Waterloo • and more.
HLE90000066

The Decade Series

SONGS OF THE 1920s
46 songs, including: Ain't Misbehavin' • Baby Face • Can't Help Lovin' Dat Man • Everybody Loves My Baby • A Garden in the Rain • Honeysuckle Rose • I Ain't Got Nobody • If I Had You • Louise • Me And My Shadow • Mean to Me • Miss You • More Than You Know • My Blue Heaven • Nobody Knows You When You're Down and Out • Show Me the Way to Go Home • Sunny • Who? • Why Was I Born? • You're the Cream in My Coffee • and more.
HLE90000077

SONGS OF THE 1930s
46 songs, including: All the Things You Are • April in Paris • Blame It on My Youth • Caravan • Cocktails for Two • A Fine Romance • Heart and Soul • I Can't Get Started with You • I'm Gonna Sit Right Down and Write Myself a Letter • In a Sentimental Mood • Isn't It Romantic? • Lambeth Walk • Moonglow • My Romance • Pennies from Heaven • Smoke Gets in Your Eyes • Thanks for the Memory • The Touch of Your Lips • The Very Thought of You • The Way You Look Tonight • and more.
HLE90000088

SONGS OF THE 1940s
53 songs, including: All Through the Day • Anniversary Song • Baby, It's Cold Outside • Besame Mucho • Blue Champagne • Boogie Woogie Bugle Boy • Diamonds Are a Girl's Best Friend • Don't Get Around Much Anymore • Have I Told You Lately That I Love You • I'll Remember April • I've Got a Lovely Bunch of Cocoanuts • It Might As Well Be Spring • It's a Grand Night for Singing • The Last Time I Saw Paris • Mairzy Doats • The Nearness of You • Oklahoma • People Will Say We're in Love • Take the "A" Train • Tangerine • Tuxedo Junction • You'll Never Walk Alone • and more.
HLE90000099

SONGS OF THE 1950s
55 songs, including: All Shook Up • Angel Eyes • Arrivederci Roma • Blue Velvet • Chantilly Lace • Climb Ev'ry Mountain • Cry Me A River • Fly Me To The Moon • Johnny B. Goode • Let It Be Me • Luck Be a Lady • Misty • Mona Lisa • Only You (And You Alone) • Peggy Sue • Que Sera, Sera • Rock Around the Clock • Satin Doll • That'll Be the Day • Three Coins in the Fountain • Tutti Fruitti • Unchained Melody • Witchcraft • and more.
HLE90000100

SONGS OF THE 1960s
52 songs, including: Alfie • Bluesette • Bridge Over Troubled Water • Can't Help Falling In Love • Crazy • Crying • Eleanor Rigby • The Girl from Ipanema • Here, There and Everywhere • If I Had a Hammer • King of the Road • Leaving on a Jet Plane • Light My Fire • The Lion Sleeps Tonight • A Man and a Woman • Moon River • Raindrops Keep Fallin' on My Head • The Shadow of Your Smile • Something • Summer Samba (So Nice) • Those Were the Days • A Time for Us • Twist and Shout • and more.
HLE90000110

SONGS OF THE 1970s
46 songs, including: The Air That I Breathe • Annie's Song • Band on the Run • The Candy Man • (They Long to Be) Close to You • Copacabana • Crocodile Rock • Dancing Queen • Don't Cry for Me Argentina • How Deep Is Your Love • I Don't Know How to Love Him • Imagine • Killing Me Softly with His Song • Let It Be • Maybe I'm Amazed • Nights in White Satin • Rocket Man • Sometimes When We Touch • You Don't Bring Me Flowers • You Light Up My Life • and more.
HLE90000121

SONGS OF THE 1980s
39 songs, including: Addicted to Love • Against All Odds • All I Ask of You • All Out of Love • Axel F • Candle in the Wind • Don't Worry, Be Happy • Ebony and Ivory • Every Breath You Take • Hard Habit to Break • I Dreamed a Dream • Longer • Love Changes Everything • Memory • Sailing • Somewhere Out There • Sweet Dreams (Are Made Of This) • Take My Breath Away • Up Where We Belong • What's Love Got to Do With It • The Wind Beneath My Wings • With or Without You • and more.
HLE90000132

HAL LEONARD EUROPE
DISTRIBUTED BY MUSIC SALES